DESIGN in the Making

resistant
materials

Steve Cushing

LONGMAN

Contents

Introduction

About This Book

This book has been written to support your Design and Technology work in resistant materials. This includes stiff and flexible sheet materials, materials that are suitable for making frameworks, mouldable materials, and electrical and mechanical components.

Design and Technology is about developing ideas for things you can make and having the knowledge, skills and understanding to make your ideas into products.

Design and Technology is a practical subject, and should be fun. It's by making things that we gain many of the skills we need to design and make new products. But it is also important that we understand the theoretical knowledge which underpins any design and technology activity.

This book contains some of the theoretical knowledge you will need to be able to design and make quality products. But you need to learn by doing, not just reading about Design and Technology. Different students learn in different ways. The book focuses on both practical skills and knowledge to allow you to use your design ability and to use correct procedures and processes. The book has been written not as a course, but as a reference point and to reinforce your teacher's practical demonstrations. Without underpinning knowledge and good making skills, designed products lack real quality. All of the photographs and pictures are of Key Stage 3 pupils' work. The process photographs are also of Key Stage 3 pupils using the relevant hand and machine tools to produce their practical outcomes.

The book contains suggestions for practical tasks: your teacher will guide you and tell you which sections of the book you should be working from. In other words, this book will be used as a resource and you will dip into it to find the necessary knowledge and skills to support the course your teacher has developed for you. Although the book has been developed for Key Stage 3, the knowledge and skills it contains are also an extremely useful resource for pupils undertaking GCSE courses at Key Stage 4.

Designing and Making

Designing cannot be separated from making. This means that when you are designing you should be thinking about how your product could be made and when you are making you should be thinking about how the product can be better designed. It is not possible to design anything without some practical knowledge of materials and the making skills needed to turn them into something useful.

You should not see designing as something you do prior to making and then forget about. When making products, you should also be thinking about changes that could be made to improve your product and how you would modify your design if you made the product again.
(Keep notes of your modification ideas for future reference.)

Your teacher will use some activities to help you to learn the skills needed to produce good quality outcomes. This may include product disassembly: you look at existing products and what they are made of. Some practical activities are aimed at giving you an opportunity to practise new skills, concepts and procedures. Other activities will enable you to put your knowledge, skills and understanding to effective use. The best way to learn is to put your knowledge and skills to the test. Don't be afraid to ask for help.

Using Information and Communications Technology (ICT)

Wherever possible you should use ICT to enhance your Design and Technology work. You can use ICT to draft out your ideas; it allows you to draft and redraft work, a vital process in Design and Technology. ICT also helps you to present your work in an orderly and effective way. CD-ROMs and the Internet provide a valuable source of information relating to design and technology.

What You Will Be Doing

As you work through the book you will be learning about making things with tools and equipment. You will learn about health and safety and acquire skills and knowledge needed to design your own products. This book will help you to learn these skills with the help of your teacher or parent.

Section 1

Safety and Using Tools

Safety

Many of the tools you use in the workshop have sharp edges. If you look after them and take care they will help you to produce high quality work. If you handle them carelessly they can cause damage, spoiling your work, injuring you or hurting other pupils.

Safety Rules

Safety rules are simple:
- Always carry sharp tools with the sharp edge pointing downwards.
- Never run around in the workshop.
- Wear an overall to protect your clothes.
- Roll up long sleeves and tuck in ties and loose clothing.
- Tie back long hair.
- Wear goggles and special clothing when necessary.
- Wear firm flat shoes.
- Small parts, scrap materials and particles from sawing and cutting can make you slip and hurt yourself. Keep the floor clean and tidy.
- Know the safety drill – how to switch off the machines.
- Always tell your teacher immediately if you have an accident.
- Do not obstruct a work area.
- Know where the emergency stop buttons are located – these switch off everything, not just the machine you are using.

Follow the safety rules in the workshop

The workshop contains danger from other sources besides tools and equipment. You should always check possible risks with your teacher and make sure that you wear the right protective clothing.

Danger From Liquids

- Spray and mist from liquids can affect your breathing and damage your eyes.
- Some liquids are toxic and can burn your clothing and skin.
- Vapours from the evaporation of liquids can be poisonous.
- Gas from liquids can be explosive.

Danger From Solids

- Dust from cutting, sanding and filing solids can affect breathing and sight.
- Smoke from burning or heating solids can be poisonous.
- Fumes from heating solids can be poisonous.
- Hot solids can be dangerous and can cause burns. Heat can result from cutting and working solids, as well as heating them directly.

Homework

Tools and machines can be very dangerous unless you follow the correct procedures for using them. You must always observe safety rules in the school workshop. The rules refer to your dress, your actions and your use of machines and materials. Draw up a list of safety points that are essential in the school workshop.

Tools and machines can be very dangerous if you do not use them correctly. You must always observe safety rules. These rules refer to your clothing, your actions and your use of machines and materials. Draw up two lists of safety considerations, one relating to the type of clothing that you should wear, and one relating to the correct use of tools and equipment. Design a poster to illustrate your safety considerations.

Tools and machines can be very dangerous if used incorrectly. You must always observe safety rules. These rules refer to your use of appropriate clothing, your actions in the workshop and your use of tools, machines and materials. Draw up a list of safety considerations under the following headings: clothing and personal safety, use of tools, use of materials, use of machines. Under each heading list six safety rules. Choose one of the safety rules and design a safety poster. Your poster must be clear, simple, but effective.

Tools and Their Uses

Tools Through the Ages

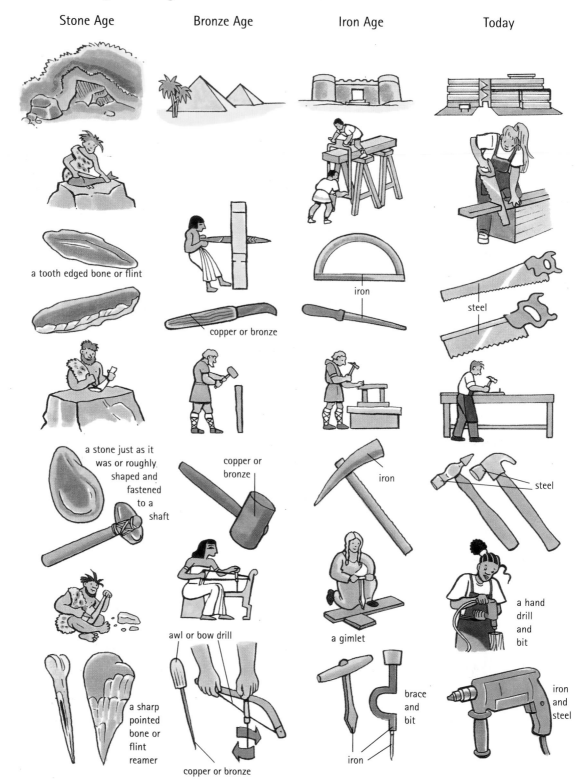

| Stone Age | Bronze Age | Iron Age | Today |

a tooth edged bone or flint

copper or bronze

iron

steel

a stone just as it was or roughly shaped and fastened to a shaft

copper or bronze

iron

steel

awl or bow drill

a gimlet

a hand drill and bit

a sharp pointed bone or flint reamer

copper or bronze

brace and bit

iron

iron and steel

Using Tools

To be good at Design and Technology you need to be able to select and use tools to shape and form materials accurately. The first tools were bare hands and sheer strength. Gradually our primitive ancestors learnt that pieces of wood and rocks that were lying around could be used as tools.

Tools have been used since the Stone Age. Considerable progress was made when stones and flints were broken and rubbed to produce a sharp edge. Early technologists used sharp flints and stones to cut through wood and chip away at rock. Cutting tools had arrived. Early hammers had stone heads bound to wooden handles. Tools have done so much for us and we should always treat them with care.

It is not known exactly when metalworking tools were invented. A gold feeding cup dating from 2750 BC was discovered in southern Iraq and metal workers are depicted in a pharaoh's wall frieze dating from 1450 BC. During the Bronze Age there was an improvement in tools. Copper and bronze heads and blades were made. But copper and bronze are quite soft and the tools must have worn down quickly.

By the Iron Age tools were much stronger, with iron heads and blades. Although the tools were strong, they were quite brittle and would break easily.

Today we use steel tools, which are strong and hard wearing.

Tools in the Workshop

The Workbench

The most important piece of equipment is the **bench**. Always keep it clean and tidy.

The bench top must be protected to ensure a good working surface

when chiselling vertically place a piece of waste wood between the work and the bench top

Bench stop

bench block

stop

when sawing in the vice place a piece of waste wood underneath

wing nut to raise and lower the stop

quick release lever

when sawing across the grain use the bench hook

when gluing, polishing or painting place a piece of waste board between the work and the bench top

Quick grip vice

handle

Bench Hook

The bench hook is used to hold work on the bench when cutting across the grain.

Using a bench hook whilst sawing

A bench hook is used for holding work on the bench when cross-cutting

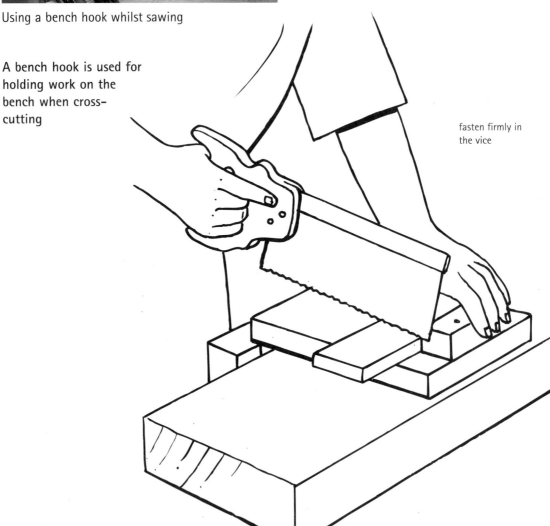

fasten firmly in the vice

Activity 1: Keep a record of the pieces of equipment you use in the workshop and their main uses. Use the following pages of the book to help you.

Marking Out Tools

One of the most important pieces of equipment in the workshop is a **steel rule**. It will help you to measure and mark out your work.

Steel rule

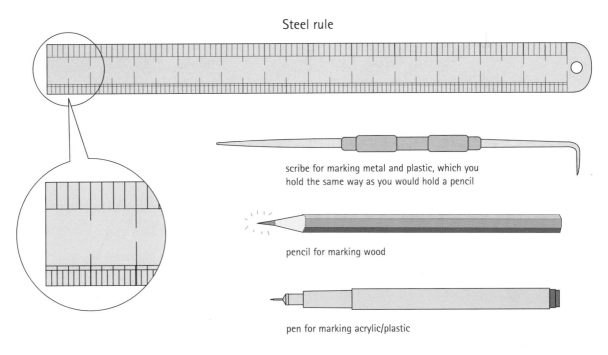

scribe for marking metal and plastic, which you hold the same way as you would hold a pencil

pencil for marking wood

pen for marking acrylic/plastic

Try and Engineer's Squares

A try square or an engineer's square can be used to check 90° angles and to mark out your work.

Try squares are used with wood. Remember to keep the stick firmly against your work using your thumb.

Using a try square

Uses of the try square

Using an engineer's square

If you are making with metal or plastic use an **engineer's square**.

Sliding Bevel

When you want to mark out or check an angle other than 90°, you can use a **sliding bevel**. A sliding bevel can be set to any angle and be locked into position with a screwdriver.

Using a sliding bevel

Activity 2: Make a list of all the marking out tools using the correct names. Now state what each tool is for.

Marking Gauges
Marking gauges can be used to mark out the width and depth of materials.

1 Release thumbscrew

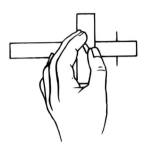

2 Slide to the required gauging distance

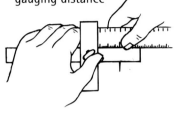

3 Tighten carefully

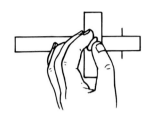

4 Test and check distance

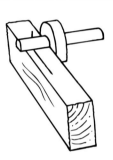

5 Mark distance

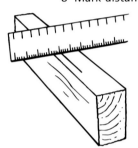

Odd Leg Callipers
Odd leg callipers are used to mark out widths and depths when working with metals and plastics.

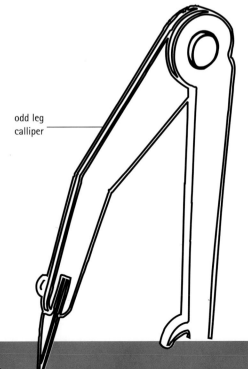

odd leg calliper

Dividers
Dividers can be used to draw curves or circles and to mark out equal distances.

Saws

You will use a range of different saws in Design and Technology. Each saw is made for a specific purpose. The teeth are an important part of a saw, they do the cutting. Generally, the smaller the teeth the harder the material the saw has been designed to cut. When you use a saw remember to use the entire blade. Do not apply too much force – let the saw do the work with long regular strokes.

Hand Saw

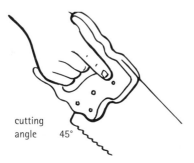

cutting angle 45°

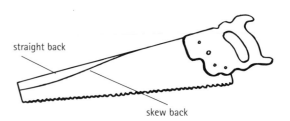

straight back

skew back

The correct way to hold a hand saw

There are two types of **hand saw** made to cut wood:
- **crosscut** for cutting across the grain
- **rip saw** for cutting along the grain.

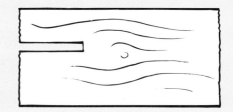

Tenon Saw

The **tenon saw** or **back saw** is used to cut small sections in wood. Remember, you can only cut to the depth of the saw's blade with a tenon saw.

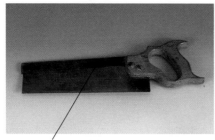

Steel or brassback

Using a tenon saw

Dovetail Saw

The **dovetail saw** looks like a small tenon saw. It is used for fine work.

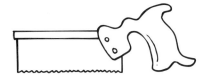

Activity 3: Draw a simple line drawing to show how you should hold a tenon saw.

Hacksaw

The **hacksaw** is used to cut metal and plastics. You can change the blade to suit a wide range of materials. The blades used for hard materials have fine teeth. The blades used to cut soft materials have coarse teeth.

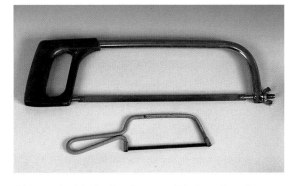

Using both hands to saw with a hacksaw

Always hold the hacksaw with two hands. Keep your work low in the vice to prevent it from breaking, bending or vibrating. Check the blade in the hacksaw before you start to use it. Use long strokes to let the blade in the saw do the work.

The vice jaws will mark your work unless you use a material softer than the one you are cutting to protect your material from damage.

A small hacksaw is sometimes called a **junior hacksaw**. A junior hacksaw is used for more delicate work.

You can turn the blade of a hacksaw through 90°. Look at the diagram opposite.

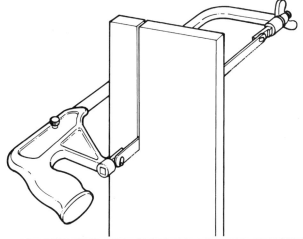

Coping Saw

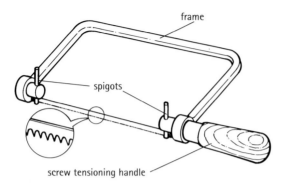

frame

spigots

screw tensioning handle

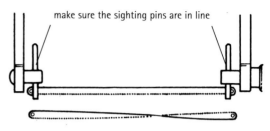

make sure the sighting pins are in line

if the pins are not in line a twisted blade will result

The **coping saw** is used to cut out curves in wood and plastic. The blade can be rotated at any angle. It can also be put through drilled holes to cut intricate internal shapes.

The blade should be put into the coping saw with the teeth facing forwards.

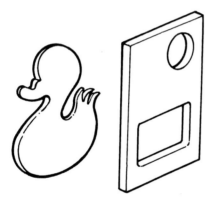

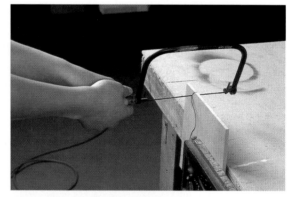

Correct use of a coping saw

Piercing Saw

The **piercing saw** is used to cut metals like copper and brass.

Safety
• Remember to guide the saw carefully and to watch your fingers.

Using a piercing saw

The Hand Drill

When you use a hand drill keep your weight behind the drill.

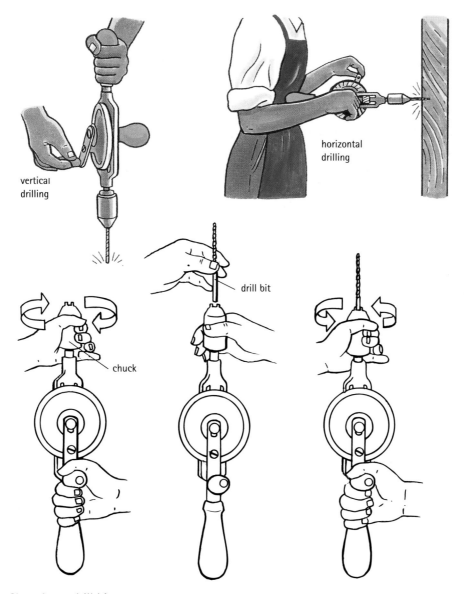

Changing a drill bit

To put the drill bit into the drill, turn the drill so that the chuck is on top. Unscrew the chuck so that the drill bit can drop inside as far in as it will go. Screw the chuck firmly onto the drill bit. Some hand drills may require a chuck key to tighten the chuck.

Files and Rasps

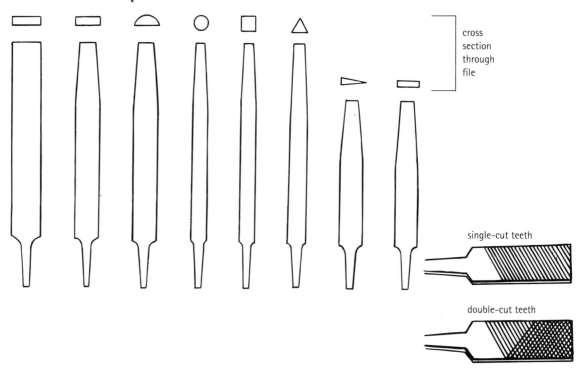

cross section through file

single-cut teeth

double-cut teeth

Files are used for shaping materials, usually plastics and metals.

They come in a wide variety of shapes and sizes, from small files called **needle files** to very coarse files called **rough cut** and **bastard cut files** for rough shaping.

The smoother the file the smoother the finished work. Files made for soft materials like wood are called **rasps**.

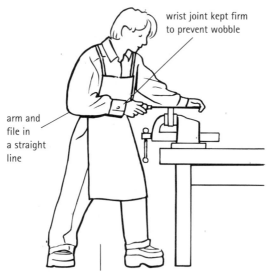

wrist joint kept firm to prevent wobble

arm and file in a straight line

legs spread to give balance and to bring the elbow to the right height

When you are using a file, the way you stand is important. You must keep the file horizontal or it will not cut square.

Use both hands to hold the file. Press on the forward stroke only. Your work should be low in the vice and should be held with vice clamps to protect it from damage.

You can get a better finish by what is called **draw filing** or by wrapping emery cloth around the file.

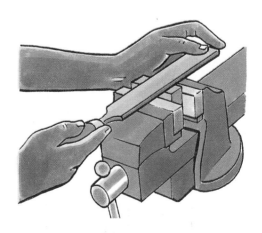

Draw filing is used to give a smooth finish.

Cross filing is used to remove a large quantity of material quickly. Generally, it leaves a rougher finish than draw filing.

The Plane

The **plane** is used to cut or smooth wood. There are a number of different types of plane but they all work in a similar way.

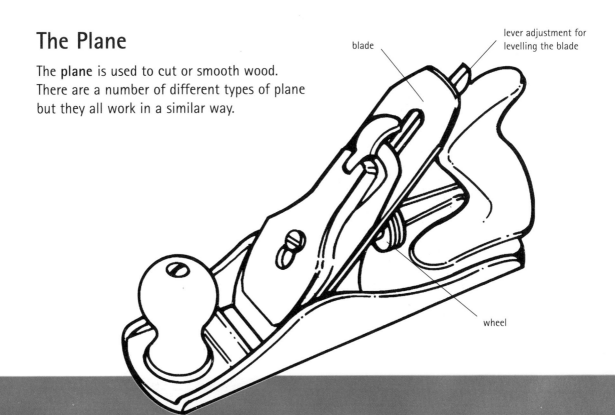

blade

lever adjustment for levelling the blade

wheel

You must make sure the blade is level before you start to use the plane. You can then adjust the depth of cut.

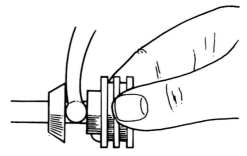

wheel for adjusting the shaving thickness

The thinner the cut and the sharper the blade, the smoother the surface of your work will be. A thin cut will also make pushing the plane along easier.

different shaving thicknesses

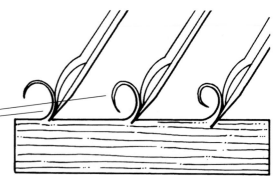

Do not put the plane down flat on the bench – remember the blade sticks out of the bottom. It is easy to damage or blunt the sharp blade. If you damage it the plane will not work properly and the finish of your work will be rough not smooth.

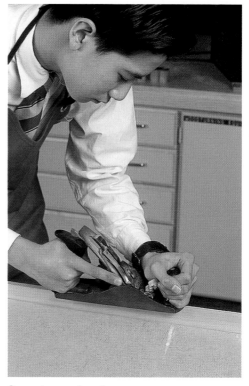

Correct use of a plane

Safety
- Remember to keep an even pressure when using the plane.
- **Never** place your hand or fingers in front of the blade.

Activity 5: List all of the tools and equipment you have used. For each piece of equipment state any special safety requirements and how it should be looked after.

Equipment	Safety requirements	Looking after it

The Chisel

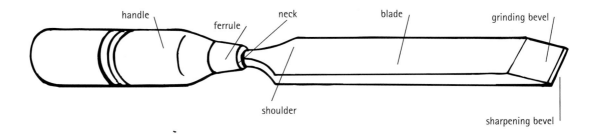

Chisels are used to cut wood. There are two types of chiselling: **paring** and **chopping**.

Paring

Paring removes small shavings. Using one hand to guide the chisel, you should press firmly keeping your shoulder over the chisel handle.

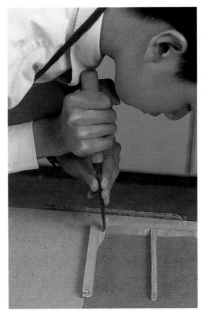

Paring

As with all sharp tools safety is important.
- Use a clamp to hold your work.
- You should never hold your material in one hand while working on it with a chisel or sharp-edged tool in the other.
- **Never** place your hand or fingers in front of the blade.

Chopping

Chopping removes large chips of wood when you hit the chisel with a mallet. Never use a hammer and always ensure your work is held firmly. Use regular strokes of the mallet, using your wrist to provide the rhythmic action.

Chopping

Abrasives

Abrasives are available in many different forms. You will probably be familiar with glass paper, sometimes incorrectly called sandpaper. Glass paper is used on wood. All abrasives work in a similar way. A hard material in grit form is held in place on a sheet of backing paper or cloth. In the case of polishes the particles are suspended in fluid.

When you rub the abrasive on your work, it removes a small amount of material. The rougher the grit and the softer the material you are working on, the more material will be removed.

You can usually tell how abrasive glass paper is by looking at the surface. The larger the grit particles the more abrasive the paper and the rougher the surface of your work will be when you have used it.

The abrasives used on metals are called **emery paper**. Some abrasives can be used wet or dry. These abrasives are called **wet and dry** or **silicon carbide papers**.

You can use abrasives by hand or on a machine

Sanding By Hand

When you are using abrasives by hand, wrap the paper around a cork block or file to keep the surface flat.

Sanding by hand

Power Tools

Sanding Machines

The **disk sander** can be used to shape and finish your work accurately. Powered machines are potentially more dangerous than working by hand. Follow the safety rules carefully.

You must always wear goggles and a face mask when using sanding machines.

Keep your work firmly on the table of the machine and ensure the disk is spinning so that your work is being pressed down onto the table. Do not press your work onto the sanding disk too hard, and always keep your work moving.

Using a sanding machine

The Belt Sander

Using a belt sander

Hold your work firmly against the stop and apply an even pressure. Wear goggles and a face mask. Only one person at a time should be using the machine.

Polishing and Buffing

The buffing machine can be used to polish shiny surfaces. It uses a polishing compound. It is not suitable for sharp or small items because the polishing wheel, called a mop, can grip the item and rip it out of your hand. **Never** polish wire or chains as they can pull your hands into the machine. If your teacher lets you use the machine, turn the machine on first then hold your work tightly and put it against the mop just below the centre line. Do not press too hard.

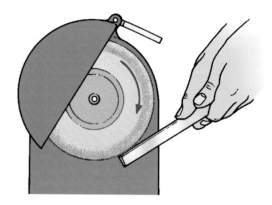

You can achieve a highly polished surface with a number of commercially produced products that are far less dangerous than the buffing machine. The secret is to give yourself enough time and to have patience. Polishing and finishing can take as long as it did to make your product. You can make your own hand powered buffing stick by gluing a piece of suede onto a stick or block.

The Pillar Drill

Before you switch the machine on, always check that the drill bit is tightly gripped in the chuck, and that the chuck key has been removed. Rotate the chuck and drill bit by hand to make sure that it has been centred correctly.

- Always clamp your work firmly.
- Always use the guard.
- Only one person at a time should be using the pillar drill.
- Wear goggles.
- Keep all loose clothing away from the drill.
- Keep your eyes on your work at all times.

Never hold the work in your hand. The work could be ripped from your grasp, injuring your fingers and throwing the work from the machine with considerable force.

Using the pillar drill

CAD/CAM

The use of computers in processing materials is called Computer Aided Manufacturing (CAM). Computer Aided Manufacture involves controlling tools and machinery with computers. The computer can control exactly where the cutting tool moves to, and when and where the machine is to cut. This enables you to produce a lot of accurate pieces that are identical in shape and size. There are a large number of different types of CAM machines in schools. Your teacher will demonstrate the machine you will work on.

When a computer is used to design objects it is called Computer Aided Design (CAD). Computer Aided Design has a number of advantages over traditional methods using a pencil and paper. These advantages are similar to the differences between handwriting and using a word processor. Designs can be changed on screen, they can be saved on disc, can be reduced or enlarged, and can be cut and pasted into other designs. Modern CAD packages allow designers to design in three dimensions. They can then rotate their designs to look at them from different angles. Another advantage is that a number of designers can work on the same design. By using the Internet these designers do not need to be in the same building, they can even be in different countries. CAD packages often automatically generate all of the drawings and parts lists necessary for manufacture. Sometimes the designs are sent direct to a Computer Aided Machine. This is called CAD/CAM. Your school may have a computer aided lathe or milling machine.

The Vibro-saw

The vibro-saw is an electrical saw which can be used on thin section timbers and some plastics.

The blade is very finely toothed and held in tension in much the same way as an electric jigsaw or coping saw. The top and bottom ends are clamped in place, the top being attached to a large curved spring, with the bottom fixed.

Inside the body of the machine is an electric motor which acts against the spring causing the blade to move up and down very quickly over a short distance. Because of this it can cut very accurately through rigid materials. One asset of this action is that the movement of the blade is not great enough to cut skin, as the skin moves with the blade. However care should still be taken as injuries can occur if fingers come into contact with the blade.

As the blades are very fine these saws can be used to cut intricate shapes, such as puzzles, following a line drawn on the work, however to avoid splitting it is advisable to stick tape to the underside of the material.

When using the saw the work must be fed into the blade with even pressure, whilst being held down onto the bed of the machine. Too great a pressure can easily break the blade, which causes the curved spring to be released. To avoid injury, do not look down onto the workpiece.

When using the saw, goggles must be worn. Remember you can use push sticks to protect your hands.

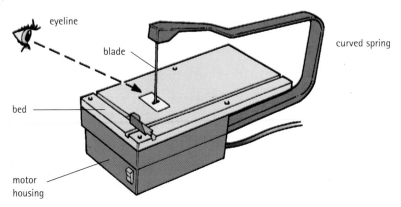

Power Tools at Home

Although you will not use them in school, there are a large number of hand-held power tools available for use at home. They can be very dangerous and all need to be used with care. Always have someone with you if you use a power tool. **Never** use a power tool at home without asking permission.

Sanding Machines

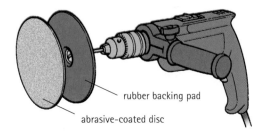

Power drill sander

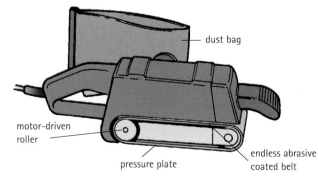

Belt sander

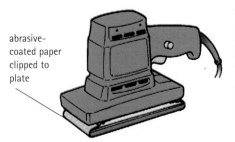

Vibrating plate sander

There are three types of sanding machine available for home use. The first uses a rubber disc fitting for a hand drill. An abrasion disc is attached to the rubber disc. The second type uses a belt and the third a vibrating plate. You must wear a mask and goggles whenever you use a powered sanding machine of any type.

For information on using a glue gun see page 78

Power Drills

Most homes have a power hand drill.

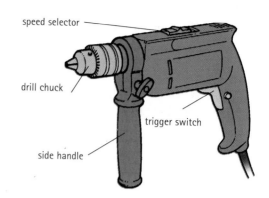

speed selector

drill chuck

trigger switch

side handle

Circular Saws and Power Planes

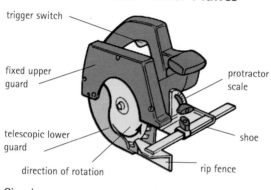

trigger switch

fixed upper guard

protractor scale

telescopic lower guard

shoe

direction of rotation

rip fence

Circular saw

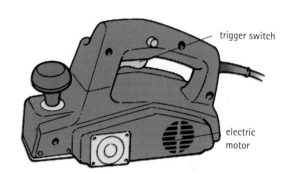

trigger switch

electric motor

Power plane

Circular saws and power planes have become increasingly popular. They are very dangerous if used incorrectly and have led to a number of bad accidents. The work must be held firmly, in a vice for example, and the power tool must be held with both hands.

Test

1. List six key safety rules that must be followed in a school workshop.
2. List the main safety hazards when working with liquids and solids.
3. What is a scribe used for?
4. What is the difference between a try square and an engineer's square?
5. Draw a bench hook and say what it is used for.
6. What is a tenon saw used for?
7. Why are the size of the teeth on a saw important? What is the difference between the teeth on a hacksaw and the teeth on a tenon saw and what materials are they designed to be used on?
8. Which way should the teeth in a coping saw be pointing?
9. Explain the terms cross filing and draw filing.
10. What are abrasives? What forms can abrasives take?
11. Why do you have to wear a mask and safety goggles when using the sanding machines? Explain the other special safety precautions you should take when using power machines.
12. Explain what a pillar drill does and why your work needs to be held firmly.

Making Things With Resistant Materials

Communicating your Design Ideas

In this section of the book we are going to look at how to improve your communication and design thinking skills. We are all designers. When we buy new clothes we are making choices about how we look. This is a design decision. The choices we make also influence fashion trends and the work of professional designers. In design and technology you are involved in designing and making objects. If the object that you are going to make is to be worthwhile, you will need to think carefully about how it is to be made, the most suitable materials, the size and shape, fashion and function. When you start designing you will need lots of ideas. You will also need to get your ideas for solving the problem out of your head, so that you can explore a range of ways of making the product. This will also enable other people, including your teacher and friends, to look at your initial ideas and help you to improve them. Getting the ideas out of your head also helps you to explore alternative solutions to the design problem, and to explore if your ideas will work in practice before you spend a long time making the design.

It is very difficult to describe the shape, proportion, form, and position of objects using only words. A picture is a much clearer way to show these things. To find out how difficult it is to describe an object using only words, ask your friend to draw the object shown in the picture through your description, without looking at the picture itself.

In the same way as different countries have different words to describe specific objects, designers have a language of their own. Of course they also use normal words, but there is a specialist vocabulary to describe tools and the way things are made.

There is also a wide range of specialist drawing languages. You will need to learn how to understand and communicate your designs using some of this specialist language. Later in this book you will explore the specialist language and drawing techniques used in electronics. Each electrical component has its own internationally recognised symbol. Similar symbols exist for flow charts, diagrams, and most engineering applications. Design ideas are best expressed using sketches, notes and specialist vocabulary.

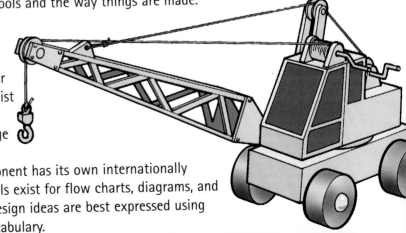

For more on product factors see pages 148–155
For more on drawing electronic symbols see pages 107–108

Design Briefs

The best way to explore the different ways that you will need to communicate your design and technology experience is to follow through a simple design and technology activity. Let's explore the design of a child's toy. The first stage is to establish what is called a design brief. The design brief tells us exactly what we are going to design. The design brief is a short statement of intent.

In this instance the designer has been asked to design a children's toy for use in a local playgroup. The toy will be designed to suit a child of four years of age. The design brief is to design an attractive and imaginative toy for use in a local playgroup with children of four years of age.

The first stage of the design process is to explore exactly what is needed. We will need to look at similar children's toys. We will need to explore what young children like to do. We could use surveys or questionnaires with potential customers, interview teachers or parents, look in books or catalogues, observe younger brothers or sisters, and search the Internet. We will then need to write down our findings in some way.

Design Specifications

Once we have conducted the research we can create a design specification. The design specification is a list showing the requirements of the toy. The design specification will contain some fixed things and some that you will be able to change through the design process. The design specification should contain at least 10 to 20 statements. This specification will include things such as:

- The toy must be safe. This means it must have no sharp corners, must not be coated in poisonous paint, must have no easily removed parts, must not break easily, no finger traps, should have no exposed dangerous moving parts.
- The toy must be fun and attractive. This means it will probably be a bright colour, attractive to a young child.
- The toy must be hard wearing.
- It must be the right price.
- The toy must be easy to maintain.
- The toy must be safe to the environment.
- The toy will be the right shape to be handled easily by a four-year-old.

Use the specification checklist to help you to draw up a specification for the child's toy described above. Part of the chart has been completed for you.

Specification

1	The toy will be a bright primary colour.
2	The toy will cost under £20 to buy.
3	
4	
5	
6	
7	
8	
9	
10	
11	
12	
13	
14	
15	
16	
17	
18	
19	
20	

Once you have decided what the product specification is, you can start to think of some initial ideas. You will need to communicate these initial ideas in some way. This is normally achieved by producing what are often called rough or initial drawings. These initial drawings are often the result of what is called a brainstorm. The important thing is to get as many ideas as you can out of your head. You can see if they will work later.

It is also possible to communicate your ideas through modelling. This can be practical modelling, using paper, cardboard, clay or other modelling materials, or a computer model. If you are using traditional drawing techniques, you do not need to worry too much about the quality of your drawings at this initial stage as long as they show your ideas clearly.

Having decided upon a range of ideas you will need to select a few of your ideas for further development. These should be your best ideas or a combination of different ideas. At this stage you may wish to use colour and other presentation methods to present your chosen ideas. Colour is one of the most effective ways of attracting the attention of your teachers and friends to your best designs. You may also wish to model your ideas, try them out, or ask somebody's opinion.

You can use any drawing technique to display your ideas, including two and one point perspective. You will learn a wide range of drawing techniques in the art department. You can use all of these techniques in this stage of your design and technology work. Colour pencils can provide an effective and cheap way of applying colour without any mess. The easiest way to highlight your chosen designs is to use colour around your drawing so that it stands out from the surrounding area. You can also colour in your design. By varying the pressure of the coloured pencil you can also add tone or texture.

You will need to develop your best solution, to make sure it fulfils the design specification.

Once you have a finished solution this should be presented using correct drawing techniques. As well as circuit diagram drawings, which you will learn about later, there is an international way of presenting design drawings for manufacture. This is called third angle orthographic projection. The word orthographic means straight drawing. (*ortho* means straight, graphic drawing).

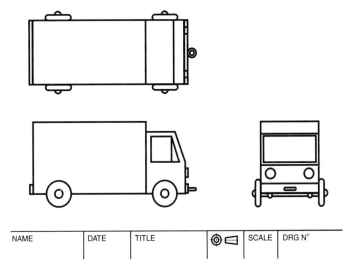

NAME	DATE	TITLE	⊚⊏	SCALE	DRG N°

Alongside your drawing you will need to create what is called a parts list. The parts list will say exactly what parts you need to build your design. It would also say if you are going to make the parts yourself, or buy them from somewhere else.

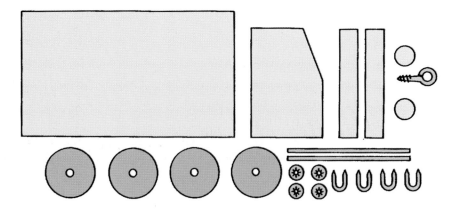

The next stage is to draw up what is called a manufacturing plan. It is important to plan the making of your product so that you can make the best use of time and resources. Your plan should show exactly what tools or equipment you need and when you need them. You could also add special safety considerations to you plan to show there are particular dangers from fumes, machines or dust. Your plan should also show how long you expect each stage of manufacture to take and the quality checks you intend to make to ensure a high quality outcome. This is particularly important in industry, where manufacturers need to work out the exact cost of the toy.

In school you will only be considering the cost of the materials, but if you are in the workplace you would be receiving a wage which would need to be added to the overall cost of the toy, as would any badly made products which need to be scraped. The other important thing that manufacturers have to consider is how much stock they need. The manufacturer needs to make sure that it has the right amount of materials and components to make the toy. They do not want any waste materials as these cost money. The materials you will be using in school have been purchased in advance by the school. The manufacturer needs to purchase the materials some time before they can sell the finished toy and recover their money.

Evaluation

Remember that a good designer evaluates, that is tests, to see if the product is of high quality and meets the design specification all of the time. Don't be afraid to change your design as you make it. The best designers learn whilst they are making their products. They then incorporate new ideas into their design. If you make a mistake this can be a good learning experience so don't try to hide it. Designs are never really finished as they can always be improved. Once you have finished your product you should test it against the design specification and then try it out in the context it was designed for, that means with a four-year-old child in this instance. You will then be able to suggest improvements. You will have become a better designer of children's toys because of the experiences you have gained.

Ergonomics

Before you can design objects for use by people you also need to understand ergonomics and anthropometrics. Ergonomics helps you to make products more comfortable, easier and safer to use. The word ergonomics comes from the Greek words *ergon* (work) and *nomos* (law).

In ergonomics we study people and the way they use products. There is no such thing as an average person. We all vary in size and shape. Data about this variation is called anthropometric data.

Manufacturers usually make clothes in small, medium and large sizes to suit different people.

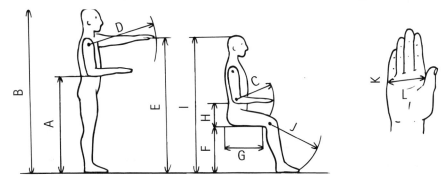

Activity 6: This table gives the measurements of an average person for the dimension shown above. Complete the table with your own dimensions.

	Average persons' dimensions	Your dimensions	Practical design and technology use
A	1060 mm		Door handles, kitchen worktops and walking aids.
B	1980 mm		Height of door, lights
C	410 mm		Distance to computer keyboard
D	650 mm		Distance to switches
E	1450 mm		Height of light switches, supermarket shelves
F	420 mm		Height of chairs and benches
G	400 mm		Depth of chairs
H	700 mm		Arm rest height on chairs
I	1300 mm		Height of car roofs
J	470 mm		Distance of car foot pedals and piano/organ foot pedals
K	185 mm		Size of computer mouse and door handle, gloves, handles etc.
L	80 mm		Keyboard layout, gloves, handles

Materials

When you design and make something you need to take into account the **working characteristics** and **properties** of the materials and components you are going to use.

Materials exist in three states:
- as raw materials
- as standard stock
- as finished products.

Raw materials, found in the earth, water and air, have to be turned into usable sheets, bars, granules and pellets. This is often referred to as **refining**. Refined materials are often called **standard stock materials** – the wood, metal, plastic and ceramics we can buy in shops to make into useful objects or **finished products**.

There are a number of ways we can turn standard stock materials like wood, metal, plastics and ceramics into objects we can use and sell. The main ways materials are shaped and formed are:
- **casting and moulding**
- **deforming**
- **cutting** – this method is often referred to as wasting
- **fabrication**.

Some materials are more suited to some of these processes than others. Designers have to consider the physical and chemical properties of materials and relate these properties to the ways materials can be worked and used.

Casting, Moulding and Deforming

In this section of the book you are going to study these methods of manufacture.

Squeezing

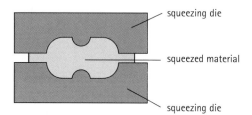

You can form material into a shape by squeezing it into a mould.

Stretching

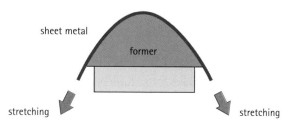

You can change a material's shape by stretching it around a former.

For more on choosing materials see pages 39–40

Pressing

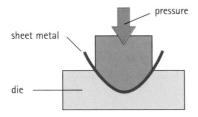

You can press a material into a mould.

Extruding

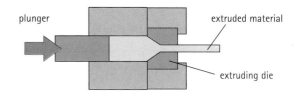

You can form material into a shape by extruding it. This will be looked at in more detail later in this section of the book.

Rolling

This method works rather like the way a rolling pin rolls out pastry. It will be covered in more detail later in this section of the book.

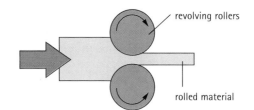

Casting

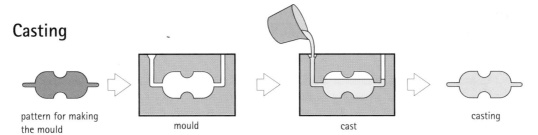

In this method the liquid material is poured into a mould and left to set. It is similar to making a jelly in a mould.

Choosing Materials

When you choose a standard stock material to make something, you choose it for a number of reasons. You could be limited by the types of materials that are available, the amount of money you can spend or your ability to use and make something with the material. The material you choose must be suited to the way you are going to make your product. You also need to consider the characteristics of the material: is it waterproof, what colours does it come in? These characteristics are called **properties**.

For more on manufacturing methods see pages 51–58

Stock Control

Designers in industry often have a list of available standard stock materials to work with. The list will also contain pre-made components. Manufacturers usually stock just enough material to keep everyone working. Keeping up-to-date with how much stock is in the material store and reordering stock when it gets low is an important job. Today a large number of stock lists are computerised. Some are automated so that the computer orders new stock automatically when stock levels get low.

You could use a computer to keep data on the materials available to you.

Material	Size	Stock level
Pine	250 × 250 mm	8 × 6 m lengths
Pine	150 × 250 mm	6 × 5 m lengths
Clock Mechanism		12 units
Copper	6 × 6 mm	9 × 5 m lengths

Aesthetics

Aesthetics refer to the way we respond to things through sight, hearing, touch, taste and smell. What a product looks like is very important. When you are designing and making things you will have to consider how people respond to what they see.

Homework

> Choose two objects from home that you like the shape of. Make a simplified drawing of them. Say why you like the shape of the objects. Also state why you think the objects are the shape they are. Is it because of fashion, or would the objects function badly if they were a different shape?

> Choose two objects from home, one that has a particular shape so that it will function correctly, and another that has a particular shape so that it is attractive. Produce a simple line drawing of each object, and then write down why you think the objects are shaped the way they are. You may wish to refer to the way the objects have been made, and the material they have been made from.

> A range of considerations including fashion, function, proportion, form, material and method of manufacture determine the shape of an object. Select three of your favourite objects from home, each should be made from a different key material. Now illustrate each object by doing a simplified drawing. Now annotate the drawings to show your understanding of the reasons why the objects may be the shape they are. The annotation must refer to method of manufacture, the purpose of the objects and the material from which the objects were made.

For more on material properties see pages 39–40

Using a Strip Heater

Skills Task

> Design and make a simple Perspex photograph frame to hold a family portrait that can be made using the strip heater and Perspex cement.
>
> Design and make a simple photograph frame made from Perspex. The photo frame must use no glue and should be made from a single piece of Perspex that will be bent using the strip heater. It must hold the photograph firmly in place.
>
> Design and make a one piece photograph frame in Perspex. The photo frame must use no glue and should be made from a single piece of Perspex that will be bent using the strip heater. Your photo frame should also be able to stack together with ten similar frames for transportation and storage. Once you have designed and made your photo frame, design a simple jig that could be made to help a manufacturer to bend large quantities of your design of the frame to the correct angles.

You are going to make your clock using a strip heater to bend a sheet of clear acrylic. You will then drill a hole for the clock mechanism and make a card insert for the clock face. You can make the insert using a computer or by hand.

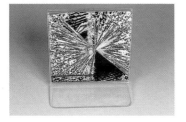 

You will need the following tools and equipment:
- electric strip heater
- a range of tools to mark out and cut the clear acrylic sheet.

Safety
- Always wear gloves.

Safety
- Observe the temperature carefully.

Using the Heater

The thermoplastic sheet should be placed on the heater with bend marks positioned over the element. Care must be taken when handling hot acrylic sheeting – remember to wear gloves.

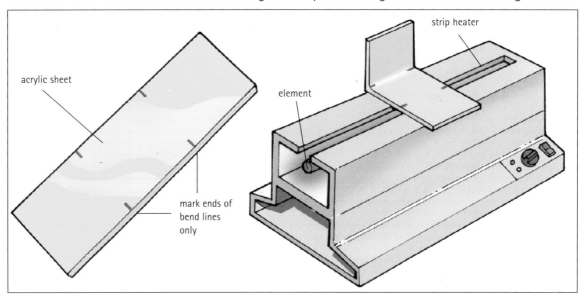

acrylic sheet

mark ends of
bend lines
only

strip heater

element

It is also possible to make the clock using a **jig**. A jig is a device which speeds up the making process and ensures that the bends are correct. If you want to make a lot of clocks a jig is a good thing to make, but you must weigh up the time taken to design and make the jig and how much time you will save by making the clock frames with the jig.

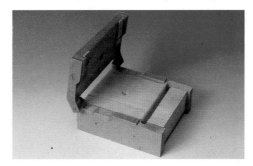

This jig was made in a school workshop to bend the clock frame and drill the hole in the right place. Notice the way the jig has to be carefully designed to take the bent sheet.

Choosing a Material with the Right Properties

The properties of materials are usually classified under different headings. This helps us to understand how different materials behave.

Strength

This refers to how hard or how easy it is to break a material. The strength of a material is usually broken down into four categories:
- **Tensile strength** – can it be pulled apart?
- **Compression strength** – will it crush easily?
- **Fatigue strength** – if it is bent over and over again, will it break?
- **Impact strength** – what force of impact (blow) can the material withstand without breaking?

Elasticity and Plasticity

This property refers to the flexibility of the material. The word plasticity comes from 'plastic' which means malleable or bendy. Plasticine is malleable as it can be bent and moulded easily. Flexible materials bend easily.

Malleability

Malleable materials can be bent, pounded and rolled into shape.

Ductility

Ductile materials can be stretched or drawn out into thin wires.

Environmental Resistance

This refers to how long a material will last in a particular environment. The ability to resist **corrosion** may be important.

Hardness

A hard material will be resistant to scratches.

Density

This tells us how heavy a material is for its size. High density materials sink in water and low density materials float.

Conductivity

Conductivity can refer to the ability to conduct **electricity** or **heat**. Materials which allow heat to pass through them are said to be good heat conductors and poor heat insulators. Similarly, materials which allow electricity to pass through are said to be good electrical conductors and poor electrical insulators.

Other Factors to Consider

Other factors which can help a designer choose a material include properties like **melting points**, the ability to add **colour** and whether the material is **magnetic**.

For more on forces see pages 41–42

Combinations of Properties

Designers and engineers are always looking for materials that are strong and lightweight.

Strength can be improved by:
- changing the shape of the material
- reinforcing the material
- making a **composite** – joining two materials together, e.g. fibreglass
- changing the **molecular** structure – the way the atoms of a material bind to each other, e.g. cold forging.

Homework

Select six household objects and state what each is made of. Now list the properties of the materials that made them suitable for being made into the household objects.

Select six household objects and state what each is made of. Now list the properties of the materials that made them suitable for being made into the household objects. You may wish to refer to texture and function. Name at least one alternative material from which each object could have been made. What are the main characteristics of the new materials that would make them suitable for that object.

Select six household objects and state the specific material each is made of. Using the terms strength, conductivity, malleability, hardness, environmental resistance, elasticity and plasticity describe the characteristics of each material and state why the designer selected the material. List at least two alternative materials from which the objects could have been made. Show the strengths and weakness of each alternative material.

Shape, Structure and Strength

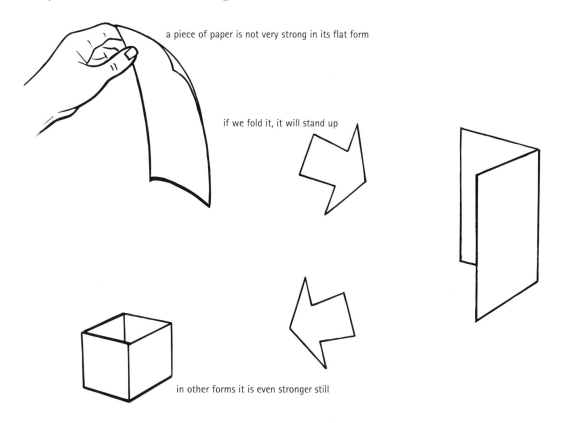

a piece of paper is not very strong in its flat form

if we fold it, it will stand up

in other forms it is even stronger still

Activity 7: See if you can fold 20 sheets of paper to make a platform which is 5 cm above the floor and strong enough to carry a heavy wooden board. Will your construction take the weight of the board?

Forces

Forces can be applied to an object in five different ways.
- compression
- tension
- bending
- shear
- torsion.

Compression

A force which causes the object to be pressed together is referred to as a **compressive force**.

Tension

A force which causes the object to be pulled or stretched is referred to as a **tensile force**.

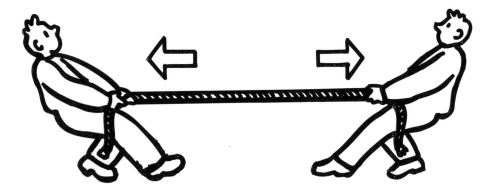

Bending

A force which causes an object to be bent is referred to as a **bending force**.

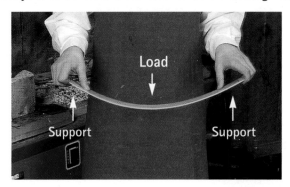

Shear

A force which acts across an object in a way that causes one part of the structure to slide over another is referred to as a **shear force**.

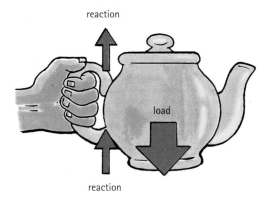

Torsion

A turning force which causes an object to twist is referred to as a **torsion force**.

In practice objects are usually subjected to a number of different forces at once. Look at the street light in the photograph right.

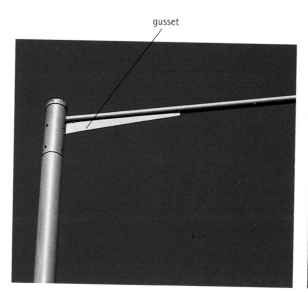

gusset

The pole is subjected to compressive forces by the weight of the light. As the light is overhanging, it will be trying to bend the post, subjecting it to bending forces. The wind will also cause the post to bend and twist, subjecting it to torsion force. Note the gusset used to support the overhanging arm and light.

Activity 8: Collect pictures of at least five everyday objects. State what types of force you think the objects are subjected to when they are being used.

Structures

Structures are very important in Design and Technology. If you examine a material with a microscope you will find that it consists of structures. This microscopic structure is what makes some materials stronger and more resistant to forces than others. When you build things you create your own structures. You need to think very carefully about the structures you build and the forces your product will have to bear. This is so that you can make products that are strong enough to do the job. You do not want your product to collapse or fall down when it is used.

There are many different types of structure all around us. Each structure has a specific purpose or function. Some structures are simple, but most are quite complicated. All structures are designed to carry the **loads** that they experience without collapsing or toppling over.

Think about the simple frame below. If we pushed hard enough on A, the frame would collapse and shear. It would not be rigid enough to take the force.

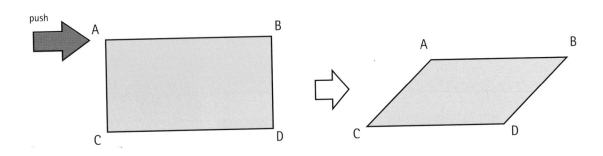

We could stop the frame collapsing by doing one of two things.

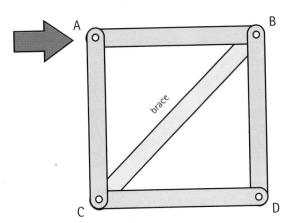

We could put what is called a **brace** into the frame. The brace would make the frame stronger because the bracing member would prevent the corners B and C from moving apart.

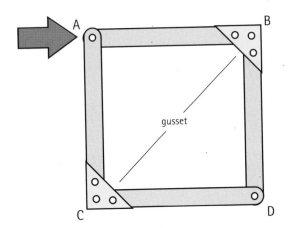

We could also strengthen the corners by putting in what are called **gusset plates** or 'webs'. The street light shown earlier used a gusset to add strength to the overhanging light and arm.

Triangles

Triangles are important as they are strong. There are lots of examples of frames which use triangles all around us. Look at the photographs shown. When you add triangle shapes to a structure it is sometimes called **triangulation**.

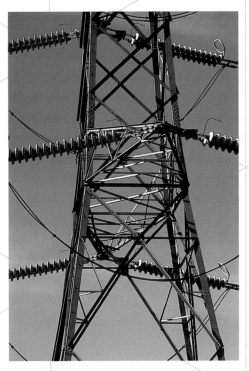

Shell Structures

Of course not all structures are made up from frames. Some people only consider buildings, bridges and similar frames to be structures. However, there are many simple objects which can also be classed as structures. That is because the shell or shape of the object itself forms a structure.

A car body is designed as a structure. This type of structure is called a **shell structure**. Shell structures are usually assembled from panels to form a protective structure. A good example would be the plastic bollards in the centre of the road. Shell structures can be man-made or natural. Whilst the material that the shell structure is made of may not be strong in itself, the way it is shaped makes it strong. The word shell gives you a clue to identifying shell structures. If you take a piece of paper it will not stand up on its own, but if you bend it into a tube it will be stronger. You have just made a shell structure.

A shell structure

The made world is full of structures including objects such as shop signs, clothing and cars. Structures exist in the natural world too. Think about the shell structures bees use when they build a honey comb.

Bees make a strong structure with a minimum of materials, retaining the maximum space possible inside the hive.

A spider uses a frame structure to give strength to its web. The spider's web is very strong in relation to its thickness.

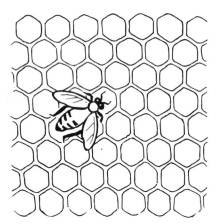

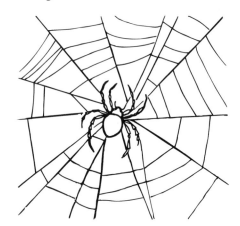

Activity 9: Find five objects that use a shell structure and five that use a frame structure. Draw and label the objects in your book or folder.

Activity 10: All structures experience compressive and tensile forces. Look at the bridge below and see if you can work out which parts are in tension and which parts are in compression.

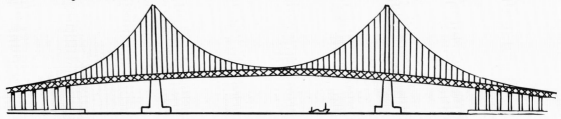

Activity 11: List as many things as you can find that use gussets or braces to add strength.

Activity 12: Look at the materials shown below. What types of forces would the different shapes be best suited to?

Materials are often sold in a range of preproduced and formed shapes. Some of these preformed shapes are designed to make the materials stronger.

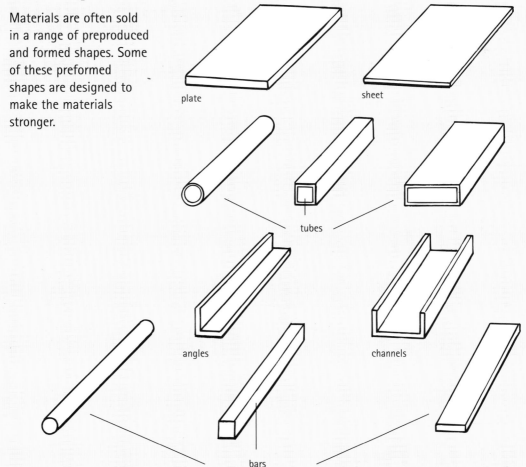

plate

sheet

tubes

angles

channels

bars

For more on forces see pages 41–44

Plastics

Plastics are popular because they are strong, light, come in a range of colours and can be made into almost any shape.

In this section of the book you are going to make a product using plastic. Plastic is an extremely versatile material. Plastics were first discovered around 1850. They were mainly used in deformation processes until the 1900s when **Bakelite** was developed. Bakelite, usually brown in colour, was used for all sorts of things like radios and hairdryers.

Bakelite hairdryer

Although Bakelite breaks very easily, its versatility changed the shape and designs of many everyday objects. By the 1920s very few homes were without some Bakelite objects.

By 1936 a new plastic, called **Perspex**, had been invented. Perspex is an **acrylic**. The invention of a material that could be clear or opaque, inexpensive, light and could be formed into complex and unusual shapes revolutionised everyday objects.

Activity 13: Carrier bags, saucepan handles, flower pots, measuring jugs, food containers, crisp packets and clothes all incorporate or are made out of plastic. Make a list of all the different things you can find that are made from or incorporate plastic. Now sort your list into groups. You could use any one of a number of categories to sort your list. For example:
- Function of the objects
- Do they bend easily?
- Do they scratch easily?
- Do they float in water?
- Or use some categories of your own.

Today there are a large number of different plastics. Although each type of plastic has a full technical name, many are referred to by their initials or by their manufacturer's name. The chart on page 49 gives examples of different plastics, what they are normally known as and what they are used for.

Known as	Full name	Used for
ABS	Acrylonitrile-butadiene-styrene	Telephones, camera bodies, vacuum cleaners and sports helmets
Acrylic	Polymethylmethacrylate	Boxes, glasses, windscreens and as a synthetic fibre in clothing
GRP	Glass reinforced plastic	Boats, car bodies, fishing rods, surfboards and canoes
PET	Polyethylene teryphthalate	Baby bottles, fizzy drink containers and as a synthetic fibre in fleece fabric and clothing
Polyester	Polyester	Car bodies, video tape and as a synthetic fibre in clothing
PTFE and Teflon (trade name)	Poly-tetra-fluoro-ethylene	Non-stick coating on cooking equipment
Nylon	Polyamides	Ropes, combs, fishing lines, gears and clothing
Polyurethane	Polyurethane	Car bumpers, trainers and used in paints and varnishes
Polycarbonates	Polycarbonates	Cycle safety helmets, car lights, CD cases, glasses and bottles
Polythene	Polyethylene, available in two types: low density and high density	Low density: plastic bags, thin plastic food containers High density: washing up bowls, toys, waste bins
PVC	Polyvinyl chloride	Signs, hose pipes, guttering, cable insulation, floor tiles and packaging
Silicone	Silicone	Printed circuit boards and sealants
Polystyrene	Polystyrene	Telephones, remote controls, light fittings, packing trays

Manufacturing Using Plastics

The raw materials used to make most plastics are coal and oil. Stock plastics are available in a large variety of forms, including powder, emulsion, resin, fluid, pellets and granules. It is hard to imagine our lives today without this very versatile material. Most plastics have no colour of their own, so coloured dyes are added.

Some plastics can only be shaped once, but others can be reheated and reshaped.

Types of plastics include:
• thermoplastic materials
• thermosetting materials.

Thermoplastic Material

Thermoplastic materials can be softened by reheating them.

Think of thermoplastic materials as being like candle wax. They can be softened and moulded into different shapes then hardened off by cooling. This can be done many times.

Thermoplastics are used in many everyday objects. These range from polyethylene, used to make a large number of our household items including children's toys, plastic bags and coating on electrical wiring, to nylon, used to make combs, bearings and stretch clothing such as tights.

Other thermoplastics in everyday use include polystyrene, used to pack and protect items and line refrigerators and freezers to help with insulation, and PVC, used to coat fabrics and produce hosepipes, packaging and drainpiping.

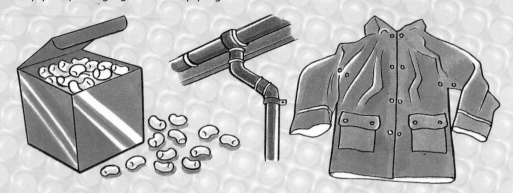

Thermosetting Material

Thermosetting materials cannot be reshaped by heat.

Think about thermosetting materials as being like the yolk and white of an egg. You can break the shell and put the egg into any shaped container to cook it. But once you have cooked the egg inside the container you cannot reheat it to change its shape.

Thermosetting materials range from phenolic resin used for electrical switches and plug covers, door handles and telephones to the epoxy resins used in adhesives and for surface coating.

Other thermosetting materials include the polyurethanes common in paints and surface finishes.

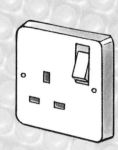

Plastics are made from the carbon found in petroleum and natural gas. **Polymers** are formed by a chemical reaction called **polymerisation**. In this chemical reaction, individual molecules called **monomers** react together to form long chains called polymers. The way that the polymers are joined together is different in thermoplastic materials and thermosetting materials.

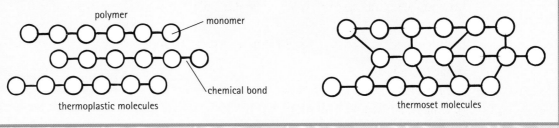

thermoplastic molecules

thermoset molecules

Thermosetting materials are usually stronger than thermoplastics. Thermoplastics are cheaper and easier to work. They can also be recycled.

You are going to learn how to manufacture an item using plastic. The method of manufacture you will use is called **vacuum forming**. Egg boxes, chocolate boxes and trays are made in this way. They are produced by sucking a sheet of warm plastic over or into a mould, then allowing it to harden.

Vacuum Forming

In vacuum forming, a thermoplastic sheet is held firmly in a frame. It is heated until it is soft. The softened sheet is sucked over a mould by removing the air around it. It is then allowed to cool.

The mould is placed in the machine and lowered using the handle

Thermoplastic sheet is firmly held in position

The heating element is placed over the clamped sheet. It remains there until the sheet is soft and pliable

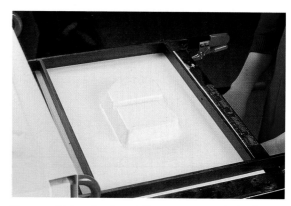

The mould is raised and the vacuum switched on

The finished sheet **must** be allowed to cool before it is removed from the mould.

Vacuum forming works in a similar way to sucking the air out of a plastic bag. Atmospheric pressure acts both inside and outside the plastic bag. By removing the air inside the bag, atmospheric pressure causes the bag to collapse. In a similar way, sucking all the air from between the mould and heated plastic results in atmospheric pressure pushing the plastic into the shape of the mould.

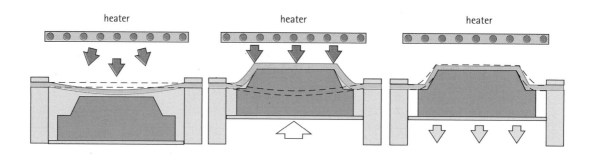

Designing a Mould or Former

The design of the vacuum forming mould is very important. As with all moulds and formers, any defect in the former will be transferred to the finished components. Moulds can be made with a range of materials, but the surface finish must be smooth and edges must be rounded off.

Consideration also needs to be given to how the component is going to be removed from the mould. This is usually achieved by putting a **draught** or **taper** on the mould of at least 3° from vertical.

It will not be possible to remove the component from this former

The component can be removed from this mould

The most important aspect of designing a mould is making it so that all the air can be sucked out between the mould and plastic material. This needs to happen quickly, whilst the material is hot and pliable, before it cools down.

Sometimes holes are drilled into the mould to prevent air from becoming trapped. This is particularly important where there are small impressions (dents) or cavities (pockets) in the surface of the mould. Where holes are drilled, they need to be extremely small or they will damage the component. They are usually 1 mm diameter on the surface of the mould, but open up to 6 mm just below the surface. This prevents restriction of the air flow.

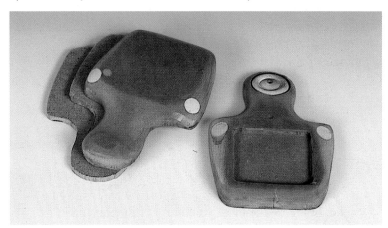

Vacuum forming moulds.

Moulds and formers are usually made of wood, but a wide range of materials can be used. Clay is an ideal modelling material. It is also possible to design inserts for moulds so that a standard mould can be modified to different designs.

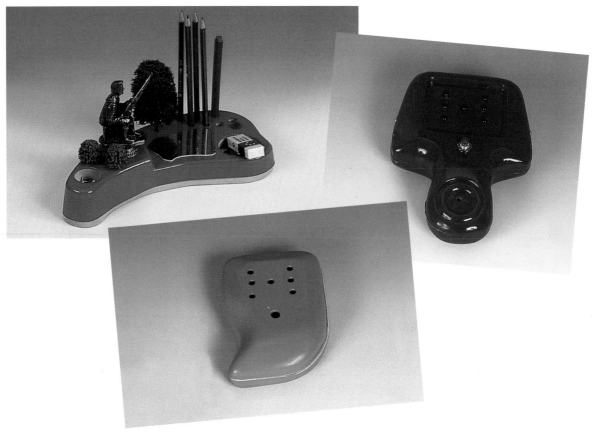

Vacuum forming products

Skills Task

You are going to design and make a simple desk tidy. Your desk tidy will be either vacuum formed or made from Perspex. Your teacher will tell you which method you are going to use. This section of the book, and your teacher, will help you to learn how to use the vacuum former or bending machine.

Industrial Methods of Plastic Forming

In industry plastic is formed into shape using a number of specialist production methods including vacuum forming. Some of the most common methods include:

- blow moulding
- calendering
- compression moulding
- extrusion moulding
- injection moulding
- laminating
- spreading.

For more on bending Perspex see pages 38–39
For more on vacuum forming see pages 51–52

Blow Moulding

Blow moulding is used to make bottles and toys. Thermoplastic material in tube form is placed inside a former where it is heated and blown up like a balloon until it takes the shape of the mould. You can see how this works by blowing up a balloon inside a pot or flower vase. Once cooled, the former is opened and the formed object is removed.

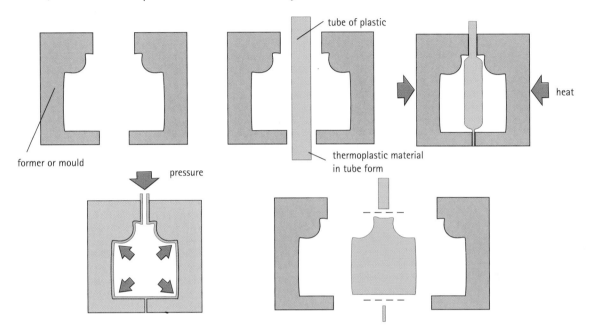

Calendering

Plastic can be rolled into thin sheets in the same way as you roll out clay and pastry. The name given to this process is **calendering**. Objects like the fabric used in plastic raincoats, shampoo sachets, plastic bags and building materials are made this way. Heated thermoplastic material is pressed between a number of heated rollers (bright drawn steel is made in a similar way). Once the plastic is the correct thickness, it is rolled through cool rollers.

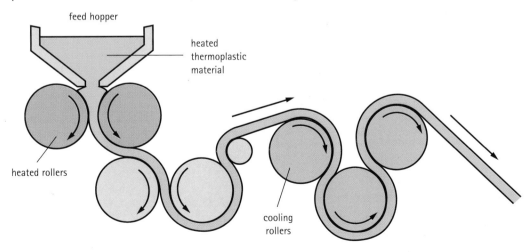

Compression Moulding

This method is used to make a number of household objects including handles, toilet seats, electrical plugs, sockets and screw type bottle lids. It is the most common moulding process. Thermosetting material, usually in powder or 'plug' form, is placed in a mould. Heat is applied and the two sections of the mould come together, pressing the molten plastic into shape.

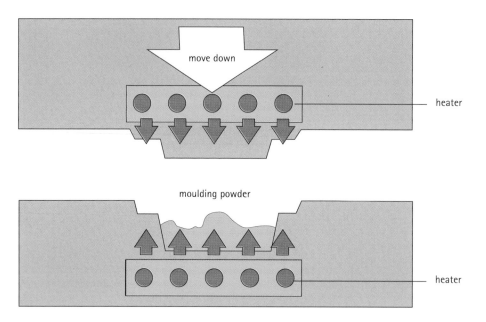

Extrusion Moulding

Long lengths of plastic can be produced in a wide variety of shapes by squeezing hot plastic through a shaped former and then cooling it down rapidly. This method, called **extrusion**, works in the same way as icing being squeezed through different shaped nozzles to decorate a cake. Extrusion moulding allows for the production of large objects providing their size and shape remain constant. Good examples of such objects are pipes, curtain rails, UPVC window frames and garden hoses.

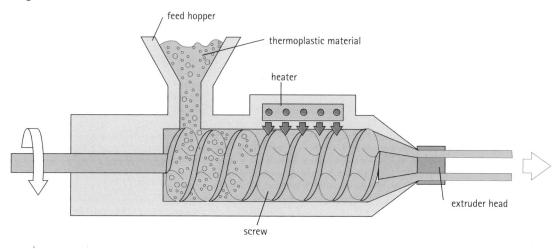

Injection Moulding

A large number of everyday objects, from telephones to buckets, are made this way. Injection moulding is used to make radio and CD player casings, watch cases and vacuum cleaners. Thermoplastic material, usually in granule form, is melted and then injected into a mould. It is left to cool before the mould is split to remove the object. Sometimes the mould is cooled by ice cold water to speed up the process.

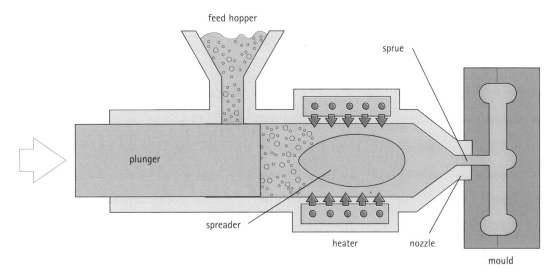

Injection moulding leaves a small stalk of plastic called a sprue, where the nozzle squirts the plastic into the mould. This has to be removed later.

Laminating

Kitchen worktops and circuit boards are often made this way. Layers of resin-impregnated thermosetting material are heated and pressed together. This causes the layers to bond.

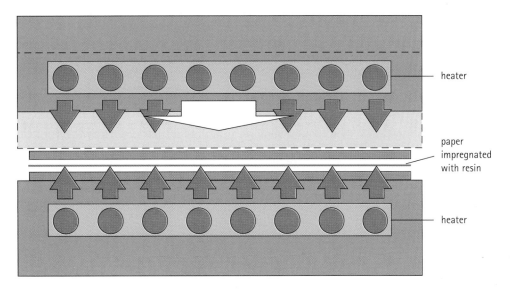

Spreading

Hot plastic can also be spread onto other materials to give a protective layer. The process is similar to spreading butter on toast. Plastic paste is poured onto a moving length of fabric or paper. This method is used to produce vinyl wallpaper, plastic backed carpets and plastic coated fabrics.

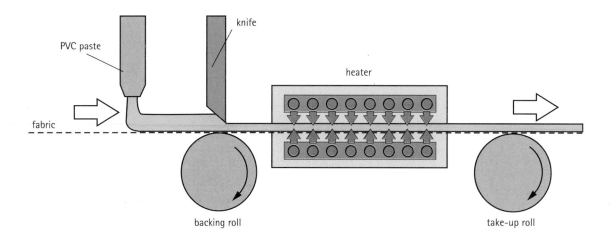

Test

1 What is standard stock?
2 What is the difference between tensile strength and impact strength?
3 Explain the term conductivity.
4 Explain the terms: casting and moulding; deforming; cutting (wasting); fabrication.
5 Explain three of the five types of forces that can act on an object.
6 What is a brace and gusset and where are they used?
7 What is the difference between a shell structure and a frame structure?
8 Explain the term thermoplastic. Name three everyday objects that are made from thermoplastics.
9 Explain the term thermosetting material. Name three everyday objects that are made from thermosetting material.
10 Describe how to use a plastic bending machine, including any safety considerations.
11 What is a jig and how can it be used?
12 Vacuum forming is one way of making products in plastics. Describe four other ways of forming products in plastic.

Design Brief

You are going to design and make a bedroom clock. Your clock should be based on a simple geometric shape. You will use a pre-made clock movement. Your clock will be vacuum formed or made from Perspex. This section of the book, and your teacher, will help you to learn how to use the vacuum former or bending machine.

You are going to design and make a simple bedroom clock for an eight-year-old child. Your clock will be based upon a cartoon character. You will use a pre-made clock movement. Your clock will be vacuum formed or made from Perspex. This section of the book, and your teacher, will help you to learn how to use the vacuum former or bending machine.

You are going to design and make a simple bedroom clock for a child who is learning to tell the time. Your clock must be attractive and educational. It must be easy to tell the time using your clock. You must use primary colours. You will use a pre-made clock movement. Your clock will be vacuum formed or made from Perspex. This section of the book, and your teacher, will help you to learn how to use the vacuum former or bending machine.

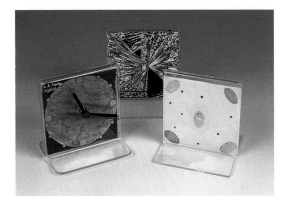

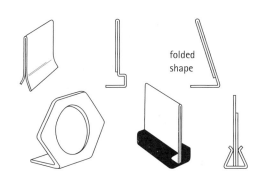

folded shape

For more on the use of the bending machine see pages 37–38.

Section 3

Wood and Joining Materials

Working with Wood

Wood is produced naturally: it literally grows on trees. The wood we use in Design and Technology comes from all around the world.

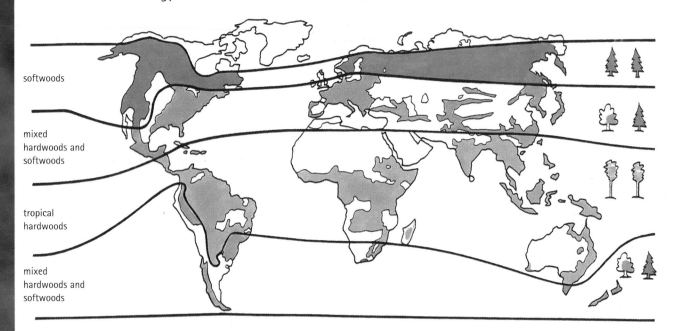

softwoods

mixed hardwoods and softwoods

tropical hardwoods

mixed hardwoods and softwoods

There are three types of wood:
- hardwood
- softwood
- manufactured boards.

In Britain we grow hardwoods and softwoods. Hardwoods take a very long time to grow. Softwoods are usually ready to cut down and use in 25 years. It is important to ensure that trees are replanted to replace the ones that are cut down. Tropical rainforests have been badly damaged: hardwoods which would take hundreds of years to replace have been cut down with no replanting.

Natural timber

Wood	Characteristics	Example Uses
Hardwoods (from deciduous trees)	• Can be difficult to shape • Heavy • Durable • Often possess attractive colours, grain and figures • Slow growing	Ash Beech Elm Oak
Softwoods (from coniferous trees)	• Usually easy to shape • Cheaper than hardwoods • Not as heavy as hardwoods • Light in colour • Fast growing	Pine Spruce

Manufactured Boards

Manufactured boards have been developed to suit different technological needs. Plywood was invented in the nineteenth century so that craftsmen could use large strong panels. In the 1940s chipboard was invented in Germany to replace natural wood which was in short supply. Manufactured boards have increased in use as natural timber has become more expensive. Manufactured boards can use 'waste' wood or **reclaimed timber**.

All manufactured boards are what is known as **composites**. This means they are made from more than one material, glue and wood fibres being the main two.

Veneer

Sometimes a thin layer of wood, known as **veneer**, is added to the outside of the manufactured board. This makes the board look like solid wood. It also adds a pattern to the board called a **grain**. The grain gives natural wood its strength.

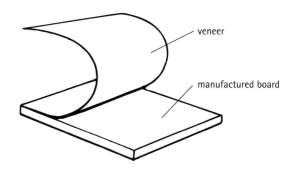

veneer

manufactured board

Plywood

Plywood is made by laminating thin sheets of wood called veneers together. The different layers, now called plies are glued with the grain at right angles. This is called **cross bonding** and makes plywood strong. Plywood is less likely to warp than natural wood and awkward shapes can be cut out without splitting. Care needs to be taken when sawing and drilling plywood because it does tend to splinter easily.

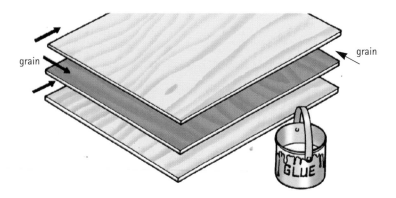

Blockboard is made the same way but the centre of the board is made from solid strips of wood, again cross bonded.

Particleboard

Particleboard is made by gluing small particles or chips of wood together. Chipboard is the most common type of particleboard.

Fibreboard

Gluing timber fibres together makes fibreboard. Hardboard and MDF are the two main types. They have no grain which makes them fairly easy to work, but the fine dust from them can be dangerous.

To make hardboard, wet fibres are pressed together and heated. The natural resin in the wood fibre acts as glue. **Medium Density Fibreboard**, known as MDF, is made from wood fibres glued with added resin and wax.

Homework

What are the differences between softwood and hardwood? Select two items, one made of hardwood, and one of softwood. Why do you think the designer selected these particular woods? What properties do the items need to have?

Explain the difference between hardwood and softwood and list the four most common types of each. You have been asked to design a garden bench. The bench will stay out in the garden all year round. The bench will be made out of wood. What wood would you recommend? What properties would the wood need to have?

Make a table to show the different properties of hardwood, softwood and manufactured boards. State the most common hardwoods, softwoods and manufactured boards. How can you tell the difference between hardwood and softwood when it is growing? Select two objects made from each (hardwood, softwood and manufactured boards) and state what characteristics the wood/board has that makes it suitable for the object selected.

Surface Finishes

Once an object has been made it needs to be finished. Natural wood looks nice but collects dirt, absorbs water and discolours easily. All materials, wood, metal and plastic need to be finished to make them last longer and look better.

Finishes can protect against:
- the elements – sun, rain, frost for example
- heat
- stains
- insects
- moisture.

The most common finishes used on wood are paint or varnish. The tools you need for the job are a paintbrush, abrasives, cork block and patience. The more effort you put into finishing the product, the better it will look.

Paint brushes are made from a wide range of materials. They usually have a wooden or plastic handle, a metal binding called a ferrule and hair or nylon bristles. If they are looked after properly they will last a long time.

Paint brushes come in a wide range of sizes. You should use the right size brush for the job.

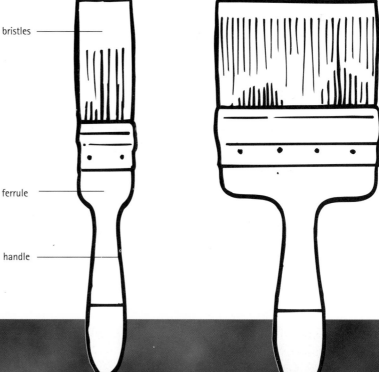

bristles

ferrule

handle

You should hold a brush the same way as you hold a pencil. Never put too much paint or varnish on the brush. The less that is on the brush the better the finish. Use a long gliding action and do not apply too much pressure.

Never leave a dirty brush without cleaning it. Do not leave a brush in spirit unless it is suspended – the bristles will curl and become useless.

Finishes can be temporary or permanent. Paint and varnish are permanent finishes. Paint can be applied to wood or metal. **Lacquers** are like varnishes and are used on metals that have been degreased first. Usually metals are polished or buffed to give a shiny surface finish. Other metal finishes include **dip coating**, in which hot metal is dipped into powdered plastic. This gives the metal a plastic coat. **Electroplating** gives the metal a coat of another more resistant metal. **Galvanising** is when iron and steel are coated with zinc. Plastics can also be polished and buffed to a high shine. Temporary finishes are usually oil or wax-based. They can be used on wood, metal and plastic. Remember to wear a mask when applying toxic paints and varnishes.

Preparing the Surface

Before you can varnish or paint wood you need to prepare the surface.

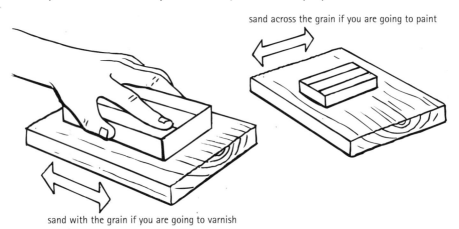

sand across the grain if you are going to paint

sand with the grain if you are going to varnish

First smooth the surface with a plane and then sand it. You must always use a cork block when you sand a flat surface. If you want to varnish the surface, you should sand *with* the grain or you will see scratches through the varnish. If you want to paint the surface, you should sand *across* the grain as the scratches will help the paint to bond with the surface.

For more on abrasives see pages 22–23

Painting Wood

Sand the surface across the grain and then dust with a clean paint brush. You should then apply **knotting** to seal any knots. This will stop the resin in the wood from coming through the paint.

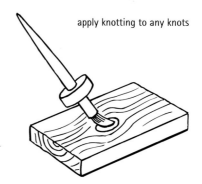
apply knotting to any knots

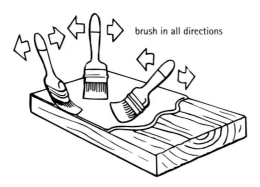
brush in all directions

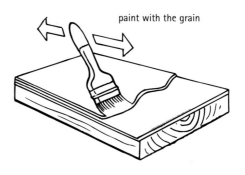
paint with the grain

Apply a coat of **primer** to seal the wood's surface. You should brush the primer in all directions.

After priming, sand lightly and dust. Then apply the final coat of paint to achieve the desired finish.

Varnishing Wood

To apply varnish, first sand with the grain.

Use a damp sponge to lift the fibres of the wood and then leave the wood to dry. Once dry, sand the wood again – sand with the grain using fine glass paper.

Once dusted, a sealing coat of varnish can be applied. Then lightly sand and dust before building up the number of coats to give the desired finish. Always brush with the grain.

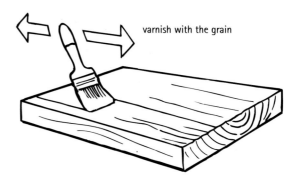
varnish with the grain

Spraying

In industry paint can be applied to metal by dipping. For example, this car body frame has just been dipped and is now being dried in a paint oven.

Paint, varnish and lacquer can be applied to wood (and metal) by spraying. This gives a totally different finish to using a brush.

As the paint particles are fine and airborne, it is important to wear a mask. Use a proper spray booth with an extractor fan when using spray paint.

Dipping

Waxing

To achieve a temporary finish you can apply a little wax or oil to a dry cloth. Rub the surface of the wood until you achieve the desired shine or surface finish.

Finishing Metal

If you want to paint or lacquer metal, the surface must be degreased and sanded with a fine abrasive like Brasso.

Activity 14: Write about two finishes, one permanent and one temporary, that could be applied to wood. Explain how the surface would be prepared and the finish applied. What are the main properties of the finish?

Homework

Look at a range of made objects and see if you can list at least three surface finishes. For each surface finish state what properties you believe the surface finish has. Why do you think the designer selected these surface finishes?

Wood and metal objects often have specialist surface finishes to enhance their properties or protect them from the elements. Select three wooden items and three metal items that have a specialist finish such as paint, wax or polish. For each of your chosen objects state the reasons for the surface finish and how the surface finish enhances the properties of the object. Your homework should be presented in chart form.

Surface finishes can be used to protect materials from the elements such as moisture, heat, erosion and corrosion. They can also enhance the properties of the material by reducing friction and by adding decoration. Select and draw a range of household items which illustrate a range of different surface finishes and annotate your drawings to show the enhanced properties as a result of the surface finish.

Joining Materials

When you make products you will need to join pieces of wood, metal and plastic together. There are lots of different ways to join materials. These pages show some of the common joining techniques. You can use these pages to help you to select the most appropriate method for your design.

Butt Joints

When you are making simple frames you will need to join two pieces of material together to make a corner joint.

The easiest way of joining any two pieces of material together is to use what is called a **butt joint**. Butt joints can be glued, welded or nailed but they tend to be weak unless the material is quite thick.

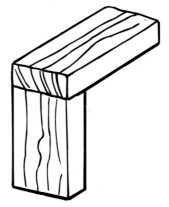
A butt joint

Reinforced Butt Joints

Butt joints can be reinforced using a **batten** or what are called **gusset plates** across the corners. Steel or plastic **brackets** can also be used.

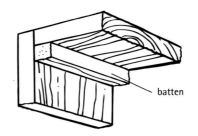

batten

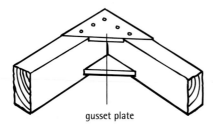

gusset plate

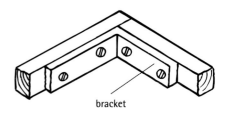

bracket

Reinforced butt joints

Mitre Joints

A **mitre joint** is stronger because it has greater contact area, compared to a butt joint.

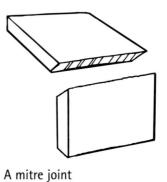

A mitre joint

Bolted or Screwed Joints

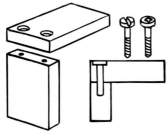

A screwed joint

When joining metal to metal the butt joint is usually bolted or screwed.

Fillet Weld

It is also possible to fix a metal to metal joint permanently by welding. The joint shown is called a **fillet weld** because the weld has filled the corner; this is called 'filleted'.

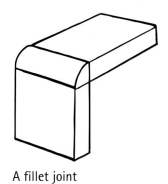

A fillet joint

Dowel Joints

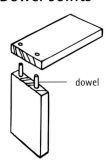

A dowel joint

Dowel joints use metal or wooden dowels to secure the two pieces together. The dowels are usually glued into position.

Tongue Joint

A thin piece of material called a **tongue** can be inserted into two saw cuts made in each piece of material. This gives a hidden join.

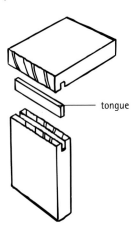

A tongue joint

Lap Joint

In a similar way to the mitre joint, the **lap joint** increases the area of contact and makes the joint stronger.

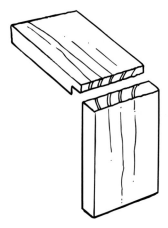

A lap joint

Dovetail Joint

There are a large number of wood joints used in traditional construction methods. The joint shown opposite is called the 'dovetail' because of its shape. It is the most common traditional joint.

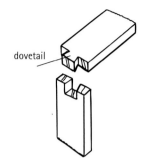

dovetail

Common dovetail joint

Cross Joints

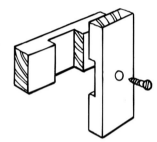

Halving joint

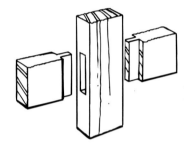

Stub mortice and tenon

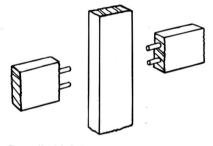

Dowelled joint

Activity 15: Look at the way everyday objects have been joined together. Draw simple line drawings in your notebook or folder. These will help you when you have to design your own products.

'T' Joints

You may want to join two pieces of material together to form what is called a 'T' joint. You can do this in a number of different ways which are shown below.

Butt joints can be nailed, welded, screwed or glued. As said before, they are not very strong if the material is thin.

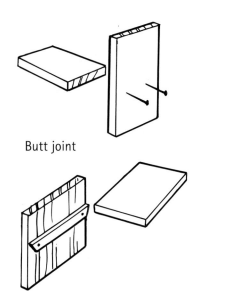

Butt joint

A batten can be used to help strengthen a butt joint.

Using a batten to strengthen a butt joint

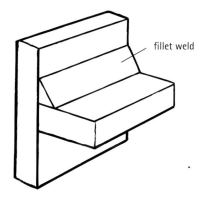

fillet weld

If you are joining metal, a weld fillet can be used

Dowel 'T' joint

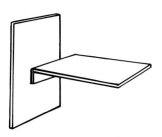

Lap joint to form a 'T'

If you can bend the material, you can make a lap joint. The increased area of contact will make the joint stronger than a simple butt joint.

Traditional 'T' Joints

There are also a large number of traditional wood joints that can be used.

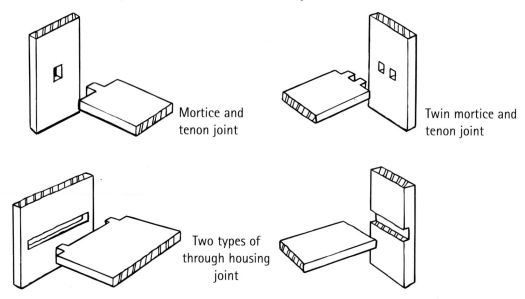

Mortice and tenon joint

Twin mortice and tenon joint

Two types of through housing joint

Fixers

Using Nails

Once you have selected a joint you will need to fix your joint together with glue, nails or screws.

There are a number of different types of nails. You can only use nails with wood.

Always select the best nail for the task

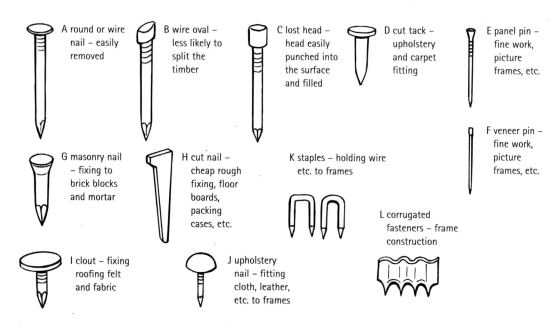

A round or wire nail – easily removed

B wire oval – less likely to split the timber

C lost head – head easily punched into the surface and filled

D cut tack – upholstery and carpet fitting

E panel pin – fine work, picture frames, etc.

F veneer pin – fine work, picture frames, etc.

G masonry nail – fixing to brick blocks and mortar

H cut nail – cheap rough fixing, floor boards, packing cases, etc.

K staples – holding wire etc. to frames

L corrugated fasteners – frame construction

I clout – fixing roofing felt and fabric

J upholstery nail – fitting cloth, leather, etc. to frames

Nails should be put into the wood at an angle to make the joint strong. This is sometimes called dovetail nailing.

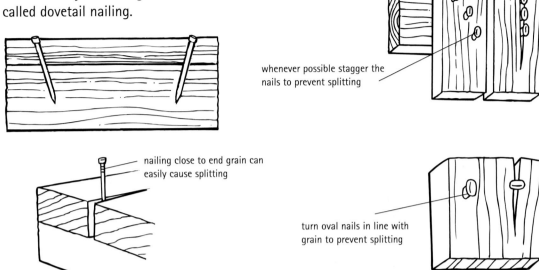

whenever possible stagger the nails to prevent splitting

nailing close to end grain can easily cause splitting

turn oval nails in line with grain to prevent splitting

Using a nail punch prevents the hammer from damaging the surface of the wood. You should always use the correct size punch for the nail head. Once knocked in, the hole can be filled with a little wood filler.

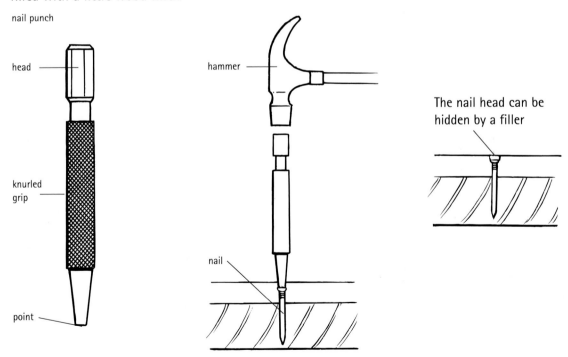

nail punch

head

knurled grip

point

hammer

nail

The nail head can be hidden by a filler

You must always nail from the thinnest material to the thickest. If you are nailing thin materials use a pilot hole first.

For more on using tools and equipment see pages 9–27

Using Screws and Bolts

There are three main types of screw which are classified by the head:

- the flathead countersunk screw
- the raised countersunk screw
- the roundhead screw.

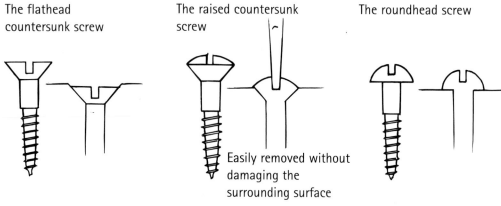

The flathead countersunk screw

The raised countersunk screw

Easily removed without damaging the surrounding surface

The roundhead screw

Screws also come in a range of different threads to suit different materials.

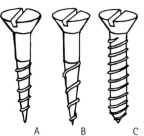

A   B   C

A wood screw; B chipboard screw;
C self tapping into thin metal and plastic

Screws come with a range of different slots, for example **slotted** and the now more common **Philips** and **Posidrive** heads. Some screw heads are also capped.

slotted   Philips   Pozidrive

Grub screws or **set screws** are used with metal and plastics and have no head.

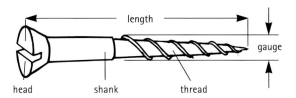

When selecting a screw you should always pick one with a length about three times the thickness of the top piece of your work.

Before using a screw, you will need to drill a **pilot hole** for the thread, a hole for the body of the screw called the **shank** and a **countersink** for the head of the screw if you are using a countersunk or raised countersunk screw.

Screws give a much stronger joint than nails and can be used in most materials. You can buy them in different lengths and thicknesses. The **gauge** number indicates the largest diameter of the screw.

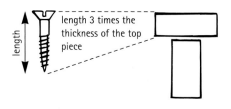

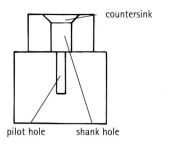

Using Nuts and Bolts

Like screws, bolts come in a wide range of shapes and sizes. The most common bolt head is a hexagon but **slotted bolts** called **cheeseheads**, **countersunk bolts** and **coachbolts** for wood with a domed head are also available. Bolts also come in a wide range of threads although the most common range in schools is ISO. In ISO threads, the diameter of the bolt is the ISO size. With so many different types of bolt it is not surprising that there are even more types of nut. It is important first to ensure that the nut is the right size and thread for the bolt. You can then choose from standard nuts, wing nuts that can be tightened by hand, flat nuts which are cheaper to buy and make, dome nuts for decoration, and automatic locking nuts which will lock themselves onto the bolt by means of either a plastic insert or a cut in the top of the bolt.

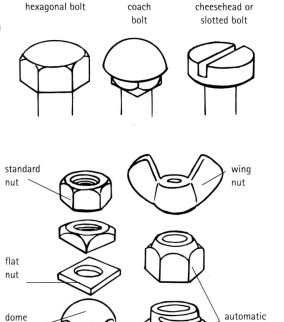

To spread the load and to prevent the nut and bolt from unscrewing it is usual to also use a **washer**.

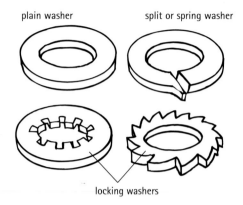

plain washer   split or spring washer

locking washers

Plain washers come in a wide range of sizes and materials from fibre to metals. Split washers, also known as spring washers, help to reduce the chance of the nut and bolt working loose. There are two other types of washer designed for this purpose. They are called locking washers.

There are two ways you can bolt two pieces of material together. One is to drill a hole slightly larger than the diameter of the bolt through both pieces of material and simply put the bolt through the two pieces.

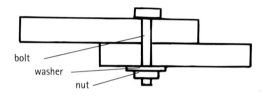

bolt
washer
nut

This method will work if the two pieces of material are thin enough to take a bolt. If one piece of material is too thick to take a bolt right through, you will need to drill a clearance hole in one piece and cut a thread into the other.

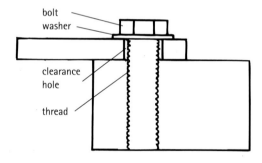

bolt
washer
clearance hole
thread

Tools for Fixers

Having decided what screw or bolts you are going to use, selecting the right tools for the job is essential.

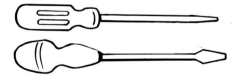

Screwdrivers come in a range of types and sizes. It is very important that you select the right size screwdriver for the screw.

For more on tools see pages 9–27

The blade must fit tightly into the screw head. If it is too thin, it will damage the screw head and the screwdriver tip. If it is too thick, it will damage the screw head and could slip out of the slot, damaging your work and causing an accident.

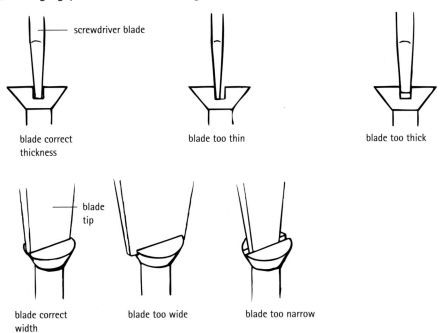

blade correct thickness

blade too thin

blade too thick

blade correct width

blade too wide

blade too narrow

Always use the correct screwdriver tip for the screw head (see page 74).

If you are using a nut and bolt you will need to use a **spanner**. There are a number of different types of spanner ranging from **open spanners** to **socket spanners**. Make sure that the size of spanner is right for the type of thread on the bolt or nut before you use it. If you do not, you will damage the nut or bolt and could injure yourself.

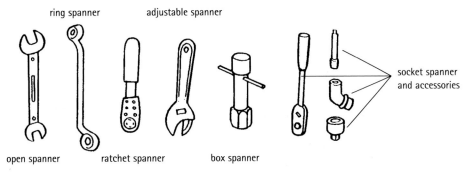

ring spanner

adjustable spanner

socket spanner and accessories

open spanner

ratchet spanner

box spanner

Using Glues
There are four main types of glue:
- Natural – these are made from animal bones and natural rubbers.
- Thermosets – very strong glues usually sold as a powder or liquid that needs to be mixed before it will set.
- Thermoplastic – sold in tubes and liquid form.
- Elastomers – usually in a rubbery liquid form, these are often called **contact adhesives**.

Brand name	Type	Drying or curing time	W*	G*	Use
Aero	Natural	6 hours	✗	✗	Wood to wood
Copydex	Latex	30 minutes	✓	✓	Acrylics to wood, metal and textiles
Resin W Unibond	PVA	60 minutes	✗	✗	Wood to textiles, metal to textiles, wood to wood
Bostick UHU	Cellulose thermoplastic	15 minutes	✓	✗	Wood to wood, wood to textiles, textiles to textiles
Araldite	Epoxy resin thermoset	60 minutes	✓	✓	Acrylics to acrylics, metal to wood, metal to metal
Bostic 3 Evo Stick	Contact elastomer	Immediate	✓	✗	Acrylics to acrylics, wood, metals and textiles
Cascamite	Urea formaldehyde	6 hours	✓	✓	Wood to wood

* W = waterproof   G = gap-filling

The **glue gun** works by heating up a solid stick of glue and melting it. The molten glue sets when it cools and can bond almost any material.

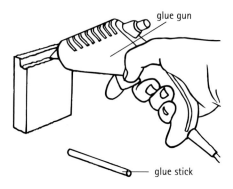

Safety
- Remember the glue from the gun is hot and can cause burns – keep your fingers clear.

Test

1 What types of wood can be grown in Britain?
2 Describe the differences between hardwoods and softwoods. Give an example of at least two types of hardwood and two types of softwood.
3 What is a veneer? Why is it useful?
4 Why is plywood less likely to warp than natural timber?
5 Explain the differences between fibreboard and particleboard.
6 Why is fibreboard used in manufactured products?
7 Why do we need to seal or finish timber products?
8 Explain why it is important to prepare wood differently depending on whether you are going to paint or varnish. Outline the preparation in each case.
9 Why is spray painting more dangerous than brush painting?

10 Describe one surface finish that can be used on metal and wood.

11 Explain what a butt joint is.

12 What advantages does a mitre joint have over a butt joint?

13 What is a 'fillet' weld?

14 Describe, with drawings, one traditional wood joint.

15 Describe, with illustrations, four different types of nail and where they could be used.

16 Describe three things you should do to prevent wood from splitting when using nails.

17 Why is a nail punch useful?

18 What are the three types of screw head? Draw each head type.

19 Draw three types of nut and two types of washer. Label each drawing.

20 Why is it important to get the correct size and type of screwdriver?

21 What are the four main types of glue?

22 Name one type of glue that can be used to stick metal and wood.

Design Brief

Cheese boards have at least two purposes. They serve as a plate or container for carrying and storing cheese, and they provide a surface on which the cheese may be cut. Using your knowledge of hard and softwood, design and make a cheese board to satisfy these requirements.

Cheese boards have at least two purposes. They serve as a plate or container for carrying and storing cheese, and they provide a surface on which the cheese may be cut. Using your knowledge of hard and softwood, design and make a cheese board to satisfy these requirements. You also need to consider an appropriate surface finish for your cheese board.

Cheese boards have a number of purposes. They serve as a plate or container for carrying and storing cheese, they provide a surface on which the cheese may be cut, and many provide a means of cutting the cheese, e.g. a knife or cheesewire. Using your knowledge of hard and softwood, design and make a cheese board to satisfy these requirements fully. You will need to consider the properties of materials and surface finishes. You should also consider the shape of the board and hygiene considerations.

Section 4

Machines and Movement

Energy, Machines and Movement

Machines use energy to perform a task. The energy source can be **electrical** or **mechanical**. In this section of the book we are going to look at mechanical energy and how it can be used to create movement. We are going to explore ways of using air, heat, gravity, flexible materials and of course human beings to create movement.

Movement

Movement can be:

- linear
- reciprocating
- rotary
- oscillating.

In **linear movement** the object travels in a straight line in one direction.

In **reciprocating movement** the object travels forwards and backwards or up and down in a straight line.

In **rotary movement** the object travels in a circular movement about a fixed point like the hands on a clock.

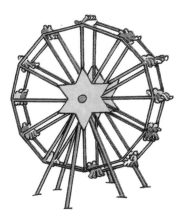

In **oscillating movement** the object moves back and forth, as in the reciprocating movement, but it follows a curved path about a fixed point.

Activity 16: Look for examples of these types of movement. Make a list of everyday objects and state what type of movement they use.

Machines

In order to design and make your own mechanisms you need to learn:
1 about putting energy into machines
2 about changing movement from one type to another.

Sources of Energy

There are various sources of energy which can be used to make machines work:

Air

- Air has been used for hundreds of years. Compressed air can be used to drive a wide range of machines. If you blow up a balloon and then let it go the air will rush out and make the balloon fly through the air. Propellers on planes use the air to pull the plane forwards, a hovercraft uses air to float across the water.

Heat

- Heat is used in steam engines to turn water into steam. This then drives pistons to make the engine work. Heat can cause some materials to explode and this can be used to produce motion.

Gravity

- Gravity is used to drive all sorts of machines. In Traditional clocks heavy weights are wound up and then drive the clock as they slowly drop. Water wheels, which are driven by falling water, can be used to turn a turbine or mill stone.

Flexible Materials

- Springs can be used to drive clocks and toys. A spring is made from flexible material that can be wound up or compressed. As it returns to its natural state its energy can be used to drive a machine.

Human Beings

- Even human beings can be used to power machines, e.g. bikes.

Homework

Heat, gravity, flexible materials like springs and humans can all be used to make machines work. Select two of these sources of energy and describe a machine that incorporates them.

Heat, gravity, flexible materials like springs and humans can all be used to make machines work. Using sketches and notes describe two machines which incorporate one or more of these sources of energy.

Using illustrations and notes show how the following sources of energy can be used to make machines work.
- air
- heat
- gravity
- flexible materials
- human beings.

The History of Machines

Early machines can be traced back to ancient Egypt. However, it was the Greek mathematician **Archimedes** who is remembered as the first mechanical scientist to record his findings and express them as scientific principles. In the third century BC he worked out the mathematical formula for simple levers that we still use today.

A machine is something that **modifies force**. When the force comes from an outside source it is called **input**. The mechanical action of the machine is called the **process**. The action the machine produces is called an **output**.

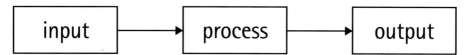

Types of Machine

There are six basic machine types:

- levers
- inclined planes
- screws
- wheels and cams
- pulleys, drives and gears
- wedges.

Levers

Almost all machines employ at least one lever. Archimedes discovered the law of the lever. He is reported to have said that if he was given a long enough lever he could move the Earth.

Archimedes divided levers into three types: first, second and third orders, which are discussed on pages 85 and 86. Each type of lever has an **input** (the **effort**) and an **output** (the **load**) along with a **pivot** called a **fulcrum**. Levers can be used to achieve what is called **mechanical advantage**.

Think about a simple seesaw in the park.

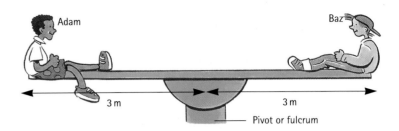

Providing the two children are the same weight, the seesaw will balance and the two children will be able to rock it back and forth about the fulcrum. When you design using levers you must remember that the end of the lever moves in the arc of a circle not a straight line. The type of movement the children make on their seesaw is, therefore, oscillating motion.

If the fulcrum moves towards one end of the seesaw this will all change. A simple mathematical formula is used to work out what happens:

$$\text{Mechanical advantage} = \frac{\text{Load}}{\text{Effort}}$$

If the distance from the fulcrum is 1 m on Adam's side and 3 m on Baz's side, Adam would have to use three times as much force and Baz would move three times as far. Put another way, we would need three Adams on our seesaw to balance out one Baz.

Levers of the First Order

A pair of scissors is a good example of how mechanical advantage can be used. Tin snips (used to cut metal) are similar to scissors but have longer handles.

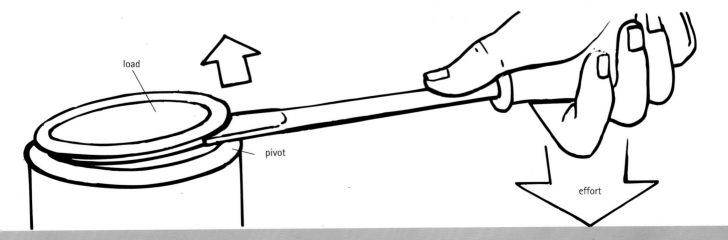

First order levers can be represented in diagrammatic form.

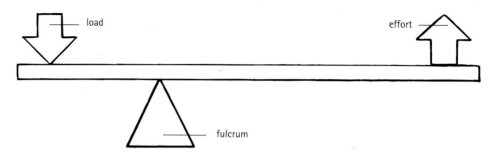

Levers of the Second Order

A wheelbarrow and nutcrackers are good examples of levers of the second order.

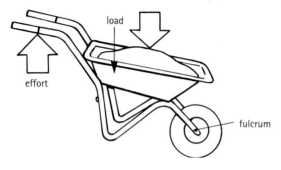

Second order levers can also be represented in diagrammatic form.

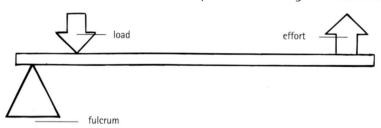

Levers of the Third Order

A lever of the third order is usually used to magnify movement. When you go fishing you will be using a lever of the third order – the fishing rod. The effort is always more than the load. Most of our arm and leg muscles also work in this way.

We can represent a lever of the third order in a diagram.

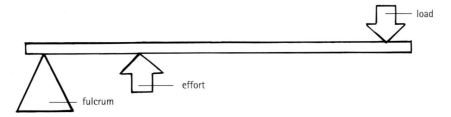

Activity 17: Look for everyday objects that use levers. Draw a picture of at least five of these objects and label the fulcrum, load and effort. State which type of lever you have drawn in each case.

Linking Levers Together

By linking levers together we can change the direction of movement. Look at the range of linkages shown below.

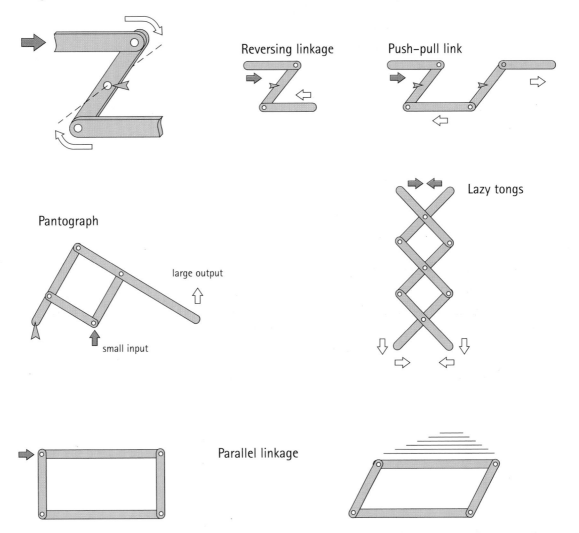

Linkages are very important in mechanical systems because they can be used to change:
1   the **direction** of movement
2   the **size** of the force
3   the **amount** of movement.

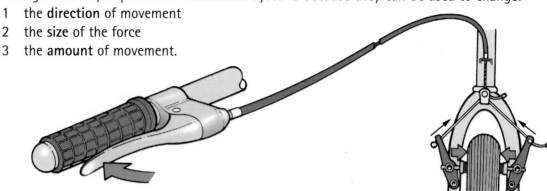

A large number of books and cards incorporate simple levers to achieve movement. Look at simple levers shown below.

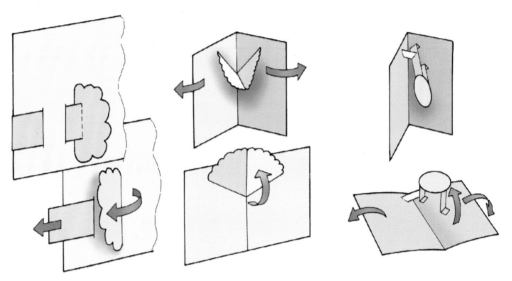

Homework

Design and make a simple greetings card that incorporates movement.

Design and make a simple greetings card, which incorporates two types of movement.

A large number of companies provide a free cut out toy on their packaging. These toys often incorporate movement, which is achieved by simple levers. You are to design and make a simple toy that incorporates both linear and rotary movement. The toy must be suitable for inclusion on card packaging with no other additional components. The pivot and all moving parts must be achieved by cutting and folding the card.

Inclined Planes

An inclined plane is simply a sloping surface. It is believed that the Egyptians built the pyramids by using an inclined plane to get the large stone blocks up into position.

Screws

A screw thread is simply an inclined plane wrapped around a cylinder.

Screw threads are used in all sorts of machines. They provide the power to lift cars in car jacks and the precision positioning in scales and instruments.

Activity 18: List as many objects as you can that use screw threads to move, grip or position things.

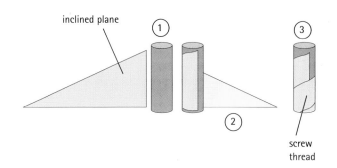

inclined plane

screw thread

Cams and Wheels

Cams

Cams are used to change rotary motion into reciprocating or oscillating motion and to change the direction in reciprocating motion.

Cams come in many shapes and sizes. All cams consist of the cam itself and the follower. An inclined plane can be used as a cam. This type of cam is called a **linear cam**. Linear cams are not used as widely as **circular** or **rotary cams**.

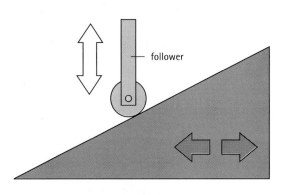

follower

linear cam

A rotary cam is an offset wheel or a wheel with shaped bumps on it. Cams are often connected to rods, levers, or springs. Most rotary cams change rotary motion into reciprocating motion.

The rotary cam diagram below right shows the difference between a normal wheel with the pivot in the centre and an offset wheel. If the wheel is pivoted in the centre, the follower stays still.

If, however, you offset the pivot from the centre, the follower will move up and down (reciprocate) as the wheel turns.

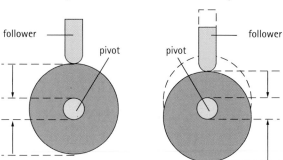

follower stays still   follower moves up and down

concentric cam   eccentric cam

Rotary cams do not have to be circular. By changing the shape of the cam the movement can be modified. The cam shown on the right is called a **pear shaped cam**.

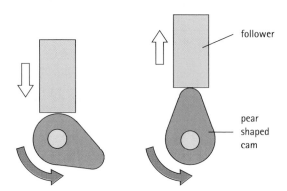

follower

pear shaped cam

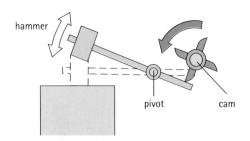

Gravity trip hammer

In the **gravity trip hammer** shown opposite, the bumps on the turning cam push down on the end of the lever making it raise the hammer again and again.

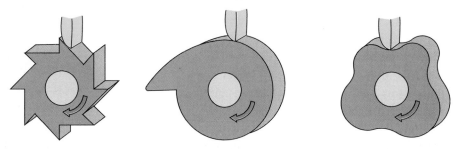

Types of cam

Cranks

A crank is simply a lever attached to a rotating shaft. A simple crank turns rotary movement into oscillating movement.

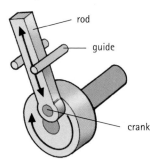

Normally cranks have an additional linkage so that they can turn rotating movement into reciprocating movement. A car engine uses a crank to turn reciprocating movement into rotary movement.

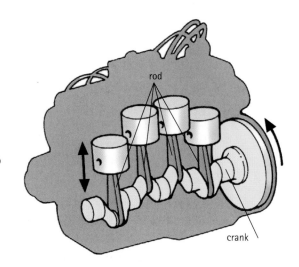

Cranks work in a similar way to cams but are usually harder to make.

Pulleys, Drives and Gears

Pulleys

Pulleys are grooved wheels. A chain or rope runs in the groove. At one end of the chain or rope is the thing that needs lifting. At the other end you put in the effort.

A single pulley simply reverses the direction of a force. When two or more pulleys are connected together, they permit a heavy load to be lifted with less force. The trade-off is that the end of the rope must move a greater distance than the load.

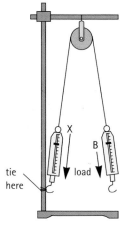

Simple pulley system

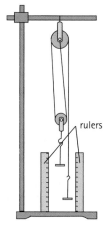

Double pulley

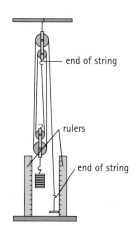

Block and tackle

In the **simple pulley** system the load will be the same as the effort. In the **double pulley** the effort needed to lift the load would be half that of the simple pulley due to the mechanical advantage created by using two pulleys. As with levers, the distance travelled by the effort will increase in line with the improvement in mechanical advantage. The **block and tackle** has been used by sailors and engineers for hundreds of years. It has even greater mechanical advantage than the double pulley.

Pulleys are used to turn linear motion into linear motion in another direction. We have already found out that cams are usually used to turn rotary motion into linear motion. It is also possible to turn rotary motion in other ways. Wheels and chains do this.

Drives

One wheel can be used to turn another: this is called a drive. If we link one turning wheel to another stationary wheel with a belt, both wheels will turn at the same speed and in the same direction.

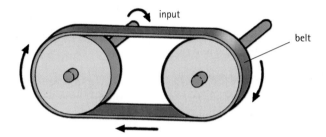

But it is possible to change the rotation of the second wheel by changing the way the belt is placed around the wheels.

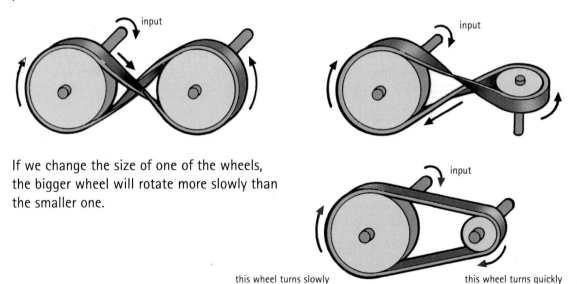

If we change the size of one of the wheels, the bigger wheel will rotate more slowly than the smaller one.

The drives shown in the diagrams above are called **friction drives** because the belt is only held onto the wheel by friction. In practice, the belt would stretch and slip. To stop this happening a **tensioner** is usually used.

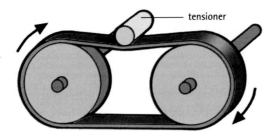

A groove or flange can be used to stop the belt from slipping off the wheel.

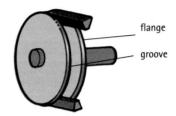

One way of making the belt grip the wheel better is to increase the friction between the belt and the wheel by changing the surface of the belt.

A **chain and sprocket** uses wheels with teeth that slot into the chain belt. This stops the chain from slipping and makes the drive more positive. This type of drive is used on bicycles.

Gears

Gears are simply wheels with teeth or pegs linked together. They do not need a belt as they usually drive each other directly. Gears mesh together to transmit motion and force.

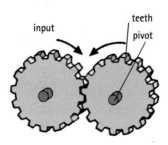

The two gears shown in the diagram on the left are the same size. Notice the way that, although the gears rotate at the same speed, they rotate in different directions. If you want the two gears to rotate in the same direction you need to add what is called an idler gear (right).

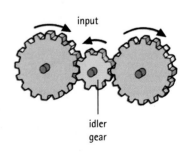

As with the belt drives, changing the size of one gear makes the smaller gear turn faster than the larger gear. The smaller one rotates with greater force. Each gear in a series reverses the direction of rotation of the previous gear.

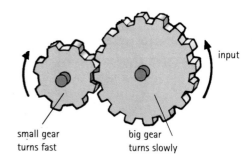

small gear
turns fast

big gear
turns slowly

input

Gears can be used in many different ways. These **bevel gears** turn the rotary movement through 90°.

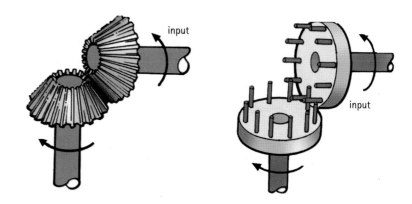

input

input

Wedges

A wedge converts motion in one direction into a splitting motion that acts at right angles to the blade. Nearly all cutting machines use the wedge. A lifting machine may use a wedge to get under the load. Twist drills also use a wedge. Early craftspeople used this principle to cut slates, cut trees and break stones.

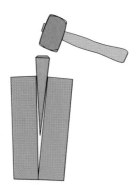

Bearings

When two materials rub together they produce **friction**. Without friction between your shoes and the ground you would not be able to walk along the street. Some materials produce more friction than others, but all materials produce some friction, even aircraft travelling through the air.

Wherever there are moving parts the designer needs to consider friction, heat and wear. The tyres on the car grip the road because of friction. Friction reduces how easily movement takes place. In this instance it is a good thing. But in a large number of machines friction has a negative effect. We do not always want materials to grip like tyres. In machines we often want to minimise friction so that the parts move more easily. We want one material to slide on the other. One way to achieve this is to use grease or oil. Some materials unfortunately soak up the oil and grip even more. Some woods do this as the oil makes the grain swell up. One way to overcome the problem is to use low friction surfaces, for example brass, some plastics or glass.

But it is not just friction which causes a problem to the designers of machines. Whenever two materials rub together they will wear down. When the two materials are made of the same material they will wear down at the same rate. This is an important consideration to the designer. Imagine the problems that could be caused by a rotating shaft if it was allowed to make the hole that supports it larger and larger or wear itself away. Eventually the shaft would be so loose that it would move up and down so much that the machine would be useless.

To overcome these problems designers use what are called bearings. There are two main types of bearing, plane bearings, and ball bearings. On a bicycle there are lots of different types of bearings. Some of them are simple brass inserts called plain bearings. Others use ball bearings in what is called a ball race.

Plain bearings

Most plain bearings are made of metal. As a general rule the metal used in plain metal bearings is dissimilar to and softer than the shaft. This causes them to wear down more quickly than the shaft. At regular intervals, as it wears, the bearing will need to be changed. The designer needs, therefore, to consider access to the bearing to enable it to be replaced. Brass and bronze bearings are common. Brass and bronze bearings usually need oil or grease to reduce the friction further. Some plain metal bearings are made by pressing a mixture of powdered copper, tin and graphite together. The graphite acts as a lubricant. This reduces maintenance as no oil or grease needs to be added during the lifetime of the bearing to keep it running smoothly.

Ball bearings and ball race

Expensive in-line skates use ball races. They take your weight and allow you to move very fast. Ball races turn very easily as the balls have a small point of contact which reduces the friction. The balls are usually held in place with a cage made from the inner and outer races. Providing the bearings are oiled well they will slip very easily.

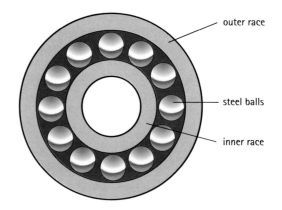

When you are making a simple bearing, you will need to make the hole larger than the shaft. But be careful or the shaft will wobble too much, preventing your mechanism from working.

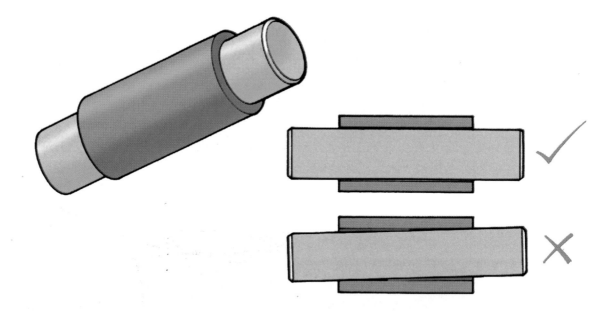

Homework

To help moving parts move freely bearings are often added. Give one example of an everyday object which uses a bearing. You may decide to look at the moving parts in a roller skate or a bicycle. Produce a drawing to show the type of bearing that is used.

Friction can cause problems for the designer when moving parts are required. Friction reduces the efficiency in machines. Explore a range of products that incorporate moving parts and produce three annotated sketches to show how the designer overcame the problem of friction.

Friction can cause problems for the designer when moving parts are required. Firstly friction causes heat but more importantly, it creates wear and causes a drop in efficiency in the machine. Explore a range of products that incorporate moving parts and produce three annotated sketches to show how the designer overcame the problem of friction. You should consider maintenance, product efficiency and cost. One of your annotated sketches must incorporate a ball bearing.

Ratchets

A ratchet is a device that allows a wheel to turn in only one direction. The ratchet wheel has specially shaped teeth. A bar on a pivot called the 'pawl' is fixed above the ratchet wheel. The pawl slides over the teeth of the ratchet in one direction, but blocks the motion of the teeth if the wheel turns in the other direction.

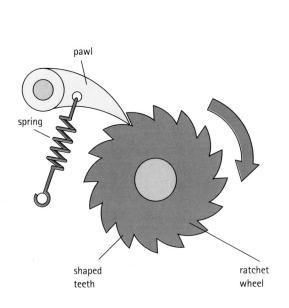

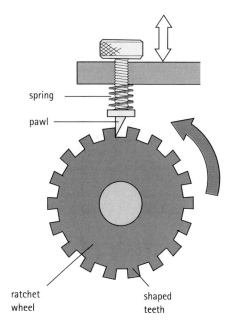

Activity 19: Look at the objects shown below. Make a simple line drawing showing how each object works. Remember to use the terms screw, cam, pulley, gears, lever and wedge.

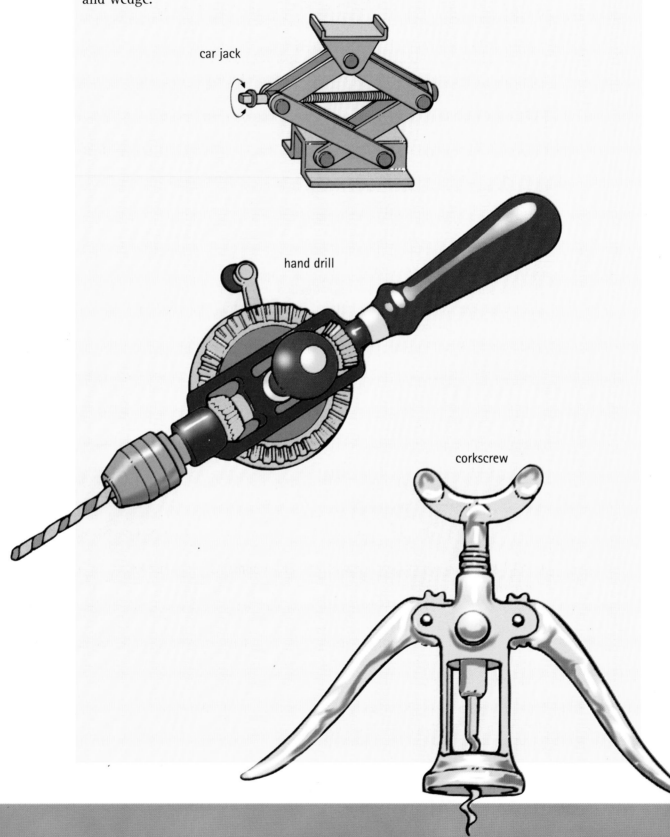

car jack

hand drill

corkscrew

Industrial Robots

A robotic system is an intelligent, automated system that has the versatility to cope with a range of tasks such as different models of car, as opposed to a dedicated automated system which can handle only one closely defined task. Robots use a wide range of levers, cams and mechanisms and they do not look like people!

The installation of an appropriate robotic system in a manufacturing process can bring significant improvements.
- Robots can improve safety by working in environments which are hazardous to humans, e.g. the welding shop of a car plant.
- Robots can improve productivity by performing labour intensive tasks, allowing skilled human workers to use their skills more effectively.
- Robots can improve quality by performing repetitive tasks to a high degree of accuracy, therefore giving human workers more time to perform more complex tasks and to check the quality of the product.

If you were studying robots you would need to learn about the mechanical systems covered in this section of the book and also how electronics can be used to control the robots' actions. Electronics are covered in the next chapter.

Your muscles are under the control of your brain. An industrial robot uses a range of **output devices** to control its levers and mechanisms. Robots also use electrical equipment like:
- electric motors
- horns and buzzers
- lights.

Just as you use your senses to tell you about yourself – whether your left arm is raised in the air for instance – and to tell you about your surroundings, so industrial robots use sensors to tell them about themselves and their surroundings. These sensors include:
- microswitches
- tilt switches
- reed and proximity switches
- light sensors.

Now you are going to learn about these things in more detail.

Test

1 Describe the four types of movement.
2 Give three examples of mechanisms which can change one type of movement into another.
3 What are the six types of basic machine?
4 Give one example of an everyday object that uses a first order lever.
5 What mechanical principle does a screw thread use?
6 Draw a pear shaped cam.
7 What is the difference between rotary and linear cams?
8 Describe how pulleys can be used to help lift heavy weights.
9 Describe the differences in speed and force between the large and small wheel shown.

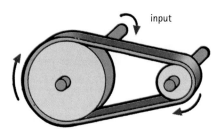

10 Describe what a crank is and where it may be used.
11 What is friction? Why is it important?
12 What is a bearing?
13 Explain why the wedge was important to early craftsmen.
14 What is a ratchet? Draw a ratchet and give one example of where a ratchet can be used.
15 What is an industrial robot?

Design Brief

You are going to design and make simple automata based upon a single cam. All students will start with the same mechanism and simple box. The box is screwed together. You can modify the mechanism to incorporate other mechanical principles.

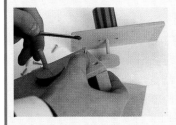

Assembling the basic mechanism

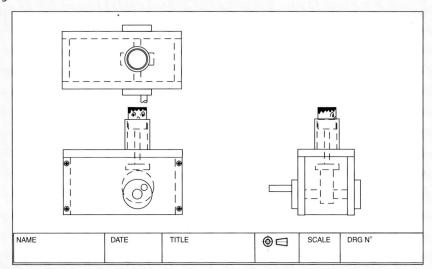

NAME	DATE	TITLE		SCALE	DRG N°

Modifications

Here is an example of an automaton made by a student

Section 5

Electronics

Design and Technology is about making things that help us to live a better and easier life. One way of achieving this is to make things **automatic**. We can do this either mechanically or electronically. In this section of the book we are going to look in more detail at electronics and electrical equipment.

Electricity

The Greeks studied electricity 2000 years ago. But it is only in the past 100 years that real progress has been made. We tend to take electrical energy for granted in our homes, schools, workplaces and communities, but it is only relatively recently that we have had electricity supplies in these places. This electricity is available from the mains supply or as batteries which are portable:

- The electricity which comes out of sockets in the wall of your house is called **alternating current** (ac). Alternating current pulses to and fro.
- The electricity stored in batteries is called **direct current** (dc). A direct current flows continuously in one direction.

direct current: dc
eg 12 $\underset{\sim}{V}$

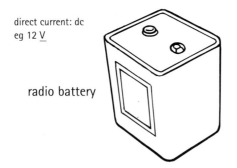

radio battery

alternating current: ac
eg 240 $\underset{\sim}{V}$ 50 H$_z$

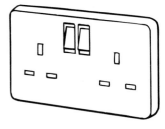

mains outlet

The Development of Electronics

In the last 30 years there has been even more rapid progress. This has led to what is now known as **electronics**.

New technology helped Neil Armstrong and Buzz Aldrin get to the moon

In 1969 Neil Armstrong was the first human to walk on the moon. New technology, some of it in the form of electronics, helped to get him there and back safely. The technology involved in electronics is changing at a very rapid pace. Each computer you have in school probably has as much computing power as NASA, the space agency which sent Armstrong to the moon, had in 1969. This is because most of the technology available in 1969 was **analogue** based: springs and gears drove all of the dials. Most of today's technology is **digital** (electronic).

As the study of electronics continues, components are being made smaller and more complex.

The first digital watch and calculator seem big and bulky to us now. They seemed compact at the time and contained many hundreds, and sometimes thousands, of electrical components.

Almost all electronic devices are made from a collection of small electronic components. By putting together a collection of standard electronic components, different electronic problems can be solved. Electronic components are assembled in an **electronic circuit**.

The name 'circuit' comes from a circular path or route. In the same way as people, cars or machines travel around a circuit from start to finish, in an electronic circuit the power travels around the electronic pathway that connects the electronic components together.

As in a race, it is important to make sure that the thing travelling around the circuit does not take a short cut. When this happens in an electronic circuit, it is called a **short circuit**. An electronic circuit needs to be designed so that the flow of electricity travels through the various components in the right way.

Design Brief

Using your knowledge of vacuum forming you are going to design and make a simple electronic toy. Your toy will have two or four flashing lights. Your toy could be a smiling face with flashing eyes, or a fish tank with flashing bubbles. Your teacher will help you to choose what you are going to design and make.

You are going to learn about electronics to design and make the circuit for your toy.

Homework

Electrical and electronic equipment is widely used in our homes. Make a list of at least eight pieces of electrical equipment that you have in your home. Now make a list of at least four pieces of electronic equipment you have in your home.

A large number of the electrical devices in our homes have automatic controls. An automatic electric kettle is a good example. It has to switch off automatically when the water boils. Make a list of all the pieces of electrical equipment you have in your home which contain automatic controls of some sort. For each piece of equipment listed, state what automatic controls it has.

A large number of the electrical devices in our homes have automatic controls. Some of these pieces of equipment are pre-set and therefore have very simple controls. An electric kettle would be one example. It simply switches itself off when the water reaches the correct temperature. Other pieces of electrical equipment, like washing machines, have a number of defined programs. Make a list of all of the things the washing machine would need to be able to sense to run through an automatic washing programme.

Automatic Devices

When designing an automatic device or piece of electronic equipment, and when programming a computer to control a device by issuing a series of commands, it is important to analyse carefully every step in the process.

The first step is to draw a **process chart**. Most process charts have an **input**, **control** and **output**.

The input is the first action that starts the system. When you switch on a light at home, the process starts with you making an electronic circuit in which electricity can flow. We will look at switches later in the book but for now let us consider the system once an input has been made. The process is what happens when you make an input. If the input is you switching on the light switch, electricity produced in a power station flows down wires to your house and then to the light bulb. The electricity then flows through thin wires in the light bulb called a filament. The filament heats up and gets hot. This is the process. Some heat energy turns into light energy to give an output – light.

The simple process chart does not give any detail to show how the system works. To show this, you need to analyse the **sub-systems** and produce another type of chart. Sub-systems are the **actions** taken and **decisions** made within the process. A flow chart is the best way to show these. A flow chart uses special shaped boxes to show what is happening. All flow charts have a start and an end.

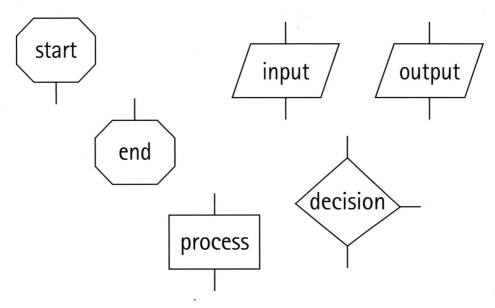

You can get a good idea of what is involved by analysing every step in making a cup of tea. The output is the cup of tea. The important bit is the control sequence in the middle.

Activity 20: Produce a flow chart using the symbols in the diagram above to show what happens when you make a cup of tea.

Activity 21: Write down an everyday activity in the form of a set of instructions. Test the instructions by asking someone to follow them. Note where things go wrong or instructions are missing. Produce flow charts of the final correct versions.

Activity 22: Compare yourself with an automatic washing machine by identifying your input devices, your programme and your output devices. Produce a flow chart to show the operation of the automatic washing machine.

For more on communicating design ideas see pages 28–32

Electronic Circuits

By grouping together electronic components in a particular way an electronic circuit can be produced. The components are usually grouped together on what is called a circuit board.

When you design a circuit you need to draw your design in a way that other people can understand. One way is to draw a simple circuit. The circuit for a common torch could be shown this way.

Whilst this type of drawing might work with a simple torch, some electronic circuits are very complicated. Rather than draw a pictorial view of a circuit, which is hard to understand, the circuit can be represented using symbols. Components are shown in the circuit by drawing different symbols to represent each electronic component. These are then linked together with vertical and horizontal lines.

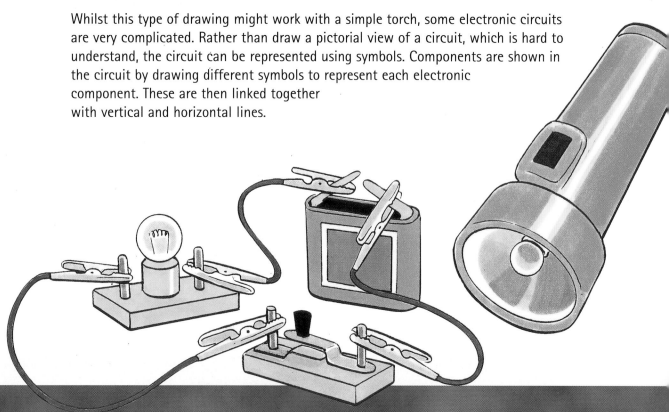

All electrical components have their own British Standard symbol.

Symbol	Stands for
—|⊢—	Cell or battery
—◯—	Bulb or light
—o⁄o—	Switch
———	Wire
—▭—	Resisters – restrict the flow of electricity
—|⊫—₊	Capacitors – stores electricity
—▶|—	Diodes – semiconductors
—◉—	LEDs – semiconductors that light up
555	ICs – Integrated circuits (silicon chips)

Let us see what the torch circuit would look like if represented using these symbols.

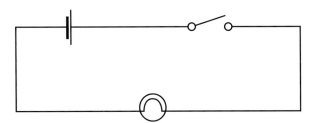

Where wires cross over each other in an electrical circuit without making a connection, there is simply a cross.

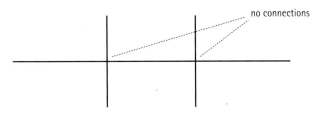

no connections

For more on communicating design ideas see pages 28–32

Where the conductors make a permanent electrical connection this is shown as a solid circle.

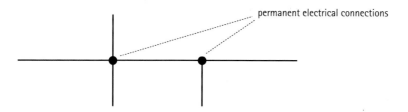

permanent electrical connections

The circuit symbol for a temporary electrical connection is a small open circle.

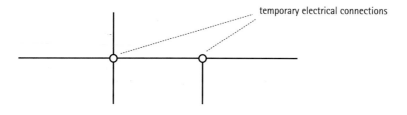

temporary electrical connections

Parallel and Series Circuits
Components can be connected in **series** or in **parallel**.

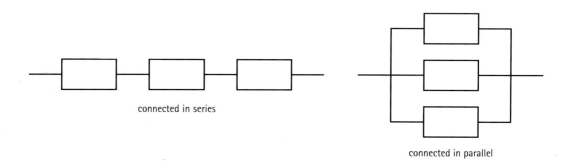

connected in series

connected in parallel

Activity 23: Draw up a simple electronic circuit to show how two light bulbs can be wired in series and then parallel to be lit by a single battery. Build your circuit on a circuit board.

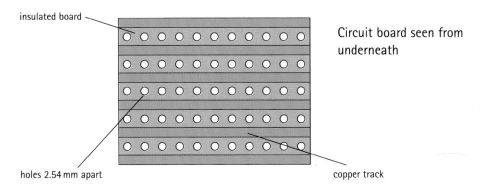

insulated board

Circuit board seen from underneath

holes 2.54 mm apart

copper track

Circuit boards have holes in them to enable you to solder the pins of the components

A circuit board has a series of strips of copper track fixed to an insulated board. Holes are drilled through the insulated board at regular intervals. When you are putting your circuit on one of the boards you will need to consider both the top and bottom of your circuit. You will have to mark out the areas of copper track that need to be removed to stop electricity from flowing past the components rather than going through them. This prevents your circuit from short-circuiting.

We need to look at the range of the different electronic components which are available to be used in your circuit.

The Range of Electric Components

Switches and Sensors

A **switch** is probably the first and perhaps the most important electronic component in a circuit. There are a wide range of switches: push switches, toggle switches, rotary switches and switches that are activated by physical events such as temperature change, water, pressure and appearance or disappearance of light.

Examples of different types of switches

Some switches are automatic, which means that you do not have to switch them by hand. They respond to things that are around them, or to changes in light, temperature, etc. This is called responding to **variables**.

Just as you use your senses to tell you about yourself and your surroundings, so some everyday objects like washing machines use sensors to tell them about themselves and their surroundings.

Activity 24: Familiarise yourself with a range of switches and sensors, which should include:
- a microswitch
- a tilt switch
- a reed or proximity switch
- a light sensor.

Although there are lots of types of switches and sensors, they all have the same function. Switches make or break contacts through which electricity flows. Sensors often vary the amount of electricity that flows through them. If we go back to our definition of a circuit as a circular path or route, when you break the circular path nothing can flow around it.

Usually switches join two points in a single conductor together, allowing the current to flow through the switch by the movement of a conductor inside the switch. In mechanical switches there is often a spring to give a snap action. Sometimes, several conductors are switched on or off at the same time. The number of conductors that can be switched at the same time is referred to as the number of **poles**. A switch capable of joining two conductors is therefore called a **double pole switch**.

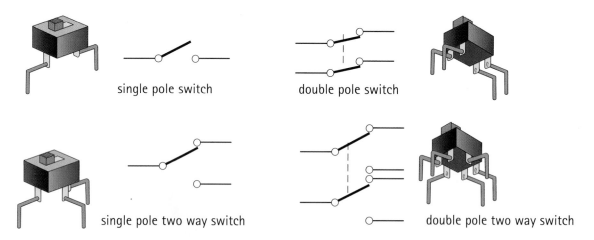

single pole switch   double pole switch

single pole two way switch   double pole two way switch

When you want to connect a single input to a range of outputs, you might use a rotary switch. As you turn the switch, a number of contacts arranged around the circle are made.

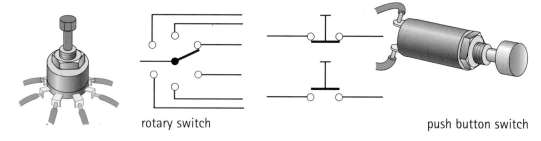

rotary switch   push button switch

Resistors

Resistors, as the name suggests, resist the flow of electricity in a circuit. Resistors will allow alternating current and direct current to pass through them. But they also restrict the flow of electricity, rather like the traffic calming methods used to restrict the number and speed of cars in towns. All materials give some resistance to the flow of electricity. Metals tend to have low resistance. This means they are good conductors of electricity. Copper has a very low resistance to the flow of electricity, which is why it is used on circuit boards.

Conductivity

A useful word to remember is **conductivity**, meaning how good a substance is at conducting heat or electricity. You can describe any material by its ability to conduct electricity or heat.

Whilst copper is a good conductor of electricity, plastic and rubber have a high resistance to electricity and are therefore poor conductors of electricity. This means it is very hard to get electricity to flow through these materials. The thickness of the material is also important. The higher the current, the thicker the conductor and the thicker the insulation needed to stop people getting a shock from it.

Electrical resistance is measured in units called **ohms**. Ohms are represented by the Greek symbol for **Omega**.

$$\Omega$$

Resistors are usually used where a circuit and its components require specific amounts of current.

There are two types of resistor available: fixed resistors and variable resistors.

Fixed Resistors

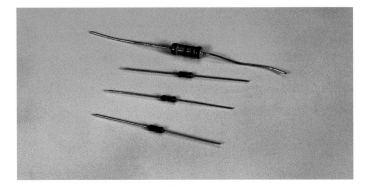

A fixed resistor looks like a tube with wire coming out of each end. Its ability to conduct electricity is constant. To show how much resistance to the flow of electricity it gives, coloured bands are put around the tube. By learning which colour refers to which number you can tell what resistance a resistor has.

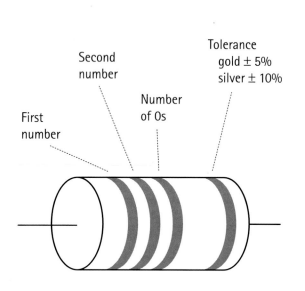

First number

Second number

Number of 0s

Tolerance
gold ± 5%
silver ± 10%

Resistance Colour Code

Number	Colour
0	black
1	brown
2	red
3	orange
4	yellow
5	green
6	blue
7	violet
8	grey
9	white

Variable Resistors

Variable resistors can be adjusted to provide a range of resistances.

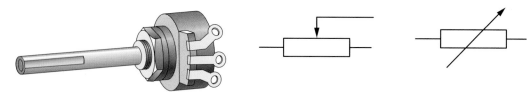

Capacitors

Capacitors are made up from layers of insulating and conducting materials. Like resistors they can be variable or fixed. Capacitors can **store** electrical charge. How much charge they can store is measured in units called **farads**, F.

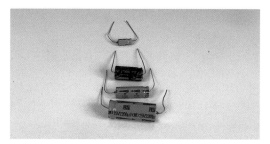

Outputs and LEDs

In the process chart we looked at what happens when you switch on a light at home. We have also looked at a number of components that can be used to make up the processing part of your system. We now need to look at the output of your system.

> **Activity 25:** You will need to explore a range of output devices, which should include:
> - an electric motor   • a horn or buzzer   • an LED.

The output to your toy circuit is a flashing light. We use bulbs in our homes for an output to a simple light circuit, but for this circuit we are going to use an **LED**.

 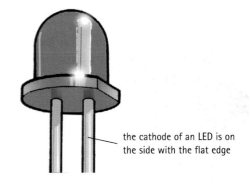

the cathode of an LED is on the side with the flat edge

LEDs

An LED or **light emitting diode** is a semiconductor diode. Diodes allow electricity to flow through them in one direction only. This means that the LED must be connected the correct way round, **anode** to positive and **cathode** to negative. The LED will only light when put in the circuit this way round and can be damaged if it is put in a circuit the wrong way round. LEDs emit light of a specific wavelength when a current flows through them. LEDs have several advantages over bulbs because they give off no heat and they respond very rapidly to changes in current. Also, they do not wear out. You do not want your toy to stop working because a bulb has blown. If you used bulbs, you would need to design the toy so that they could be replaced.

LEDs are available in a wide variety of colours including red, yellow, orange, green and blue.

Sometimes normal diodes are put into a circuit to protect the LED. All LEDs have some method of identifying which pin is the anode and which is the cathode. Usually the cathode is identified by a flat surface on the body of the LED.

Using a Soldering Iron

You will need to use a soldering iron to fix your components to the circuit board. This will ensure a good electrical contact between the component and the board. If you do not do this, the point of contact will resist the flow of electricity. Soldering irons get very hot and can be dangerous if used incorrectly.

Every time you use a soldering iron you must always be aware of safety issues.
- You must be careful to avoid burning the leads.
- Always place the soldering iron in the stand when you are not using it.
- You must never leave the soldering iron lying on the bench.
- Do not wave the soldering iron around when it is not being used.
- Be careful and do not burn your fingers.

Before you solder your components to the board, you will need to clean the pins on the components. This is achieved by rubbing the pins with some fine wire wool.

The soldering iron bit will get hot almost as soon as it is plugged in. It will need to be 'tinned' before it can be used. Tinning is achieved by putting a small amount of solder on the end of the soldering iron, or by wetting the hot tip.

The **solder** used for electronics is hollow and has **flux** inside. The flux helps the solder to flow and keeps the joint clean while you are soldering it.

To obtain a good soldered joint it is important to ensure that the work is heated properly. Do not try to rush. If you do not achieve the correct heat, you will not have a good electrical contact between the component and the board.

Some components, such as LEDs, are easily damaged by heat. It is advisable to use a small pair of pliers to hold the components in place and to act as a heat sink. A heat sink helps to take away the heat from a hot area. If you put pliers between the component and the place in which you are soldering, they will remove the heat before it can damage the fragile component.

 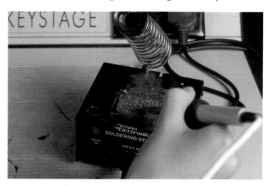

When soldering it is best to hold the soldering iron tip onto the copper track close to the component, but not touching it. Next put the solder onto the copper track near the iron tip. When the work is hot enough, the solder will melt and flow. At this point you should move the soldering iron tip around the component. This will ensure that the pins are correctly joined to the copper track.

For more on safety see pages 23–24

Activity 26: If you follow this step-by-step guide you will produce a simple circuit with an LED.

1 Draw a circuit and work out the value of any components you will need. For this example you will need:

   1 × LED

   1 × resistor (value 470 Ω).

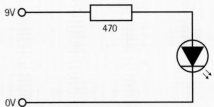

2 Produce a plan view of a circuit board showing where your components will go. Use strip board (vero board) paper. Make sure you indicate which way the tracks are running.

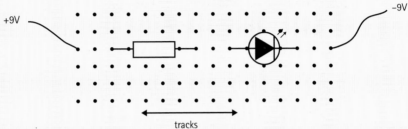

3 Now glue the plan view on to the strip board (vero board). Making sure that the dots line up with the holes in the board, carefully place your components in the strip board according to the plan.

4 Turn the strip board over without letting the components fall out. Use a permanent marker to mark the copper track that runs from one side of the component to the other.

5 Carefully remove the components from the strip board and place them somewhere safe (do not lose them).

6 Using the hand-held countersink remove the areas of track that you have marked so that the current will not bypass the component.

7 When this is done, you will be able to place the components through from the top side and solder them in place.

Microelectronics

Integrated Circuits

Large glass-enclosed electronic components called **valves** were used in early electronic equipment. They made the equipment big and bulky by modern standards. By 1955 **transistors** were replacing valves. They work in a similar way to valves but are made of silicon. **Silicon chips** have replaced bulky valves and are common in most modern electronic equipment. When it was discovered that it was possible to get two or three transistors on one single piece of silicon, microelectronics was born.

One of the reasons that objects incorporating electronic circuits became smaller and more compact is the introduction of **integrated circuits**. Integrated circuits are also known as **ICs**.

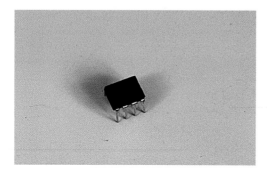
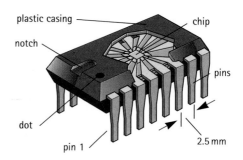

In the ICs that are made today there are many thousands of components such as transistors, diodes, resistors and capacitors, all packed onto one small silicon chip.

Silicon chips are normally packed in black plastic. The pins are usually in two parallel lines. Each pin is connected to the circuit through an IC holder which has exactly the same number of pins. While most ICs look exactly the same, they have letters and numbers on them so you know what they are. They also have a small dot or notch at one end to distinguish one end from the other.

The IC you will be using as part of your circuit is known as a 555 timer. This is a fairly simple IC timer that can be used in many different ways to control the timing in circuits. The timers operate at between 3–18V. The 555 timer can be used in two ways: as a **monostable** or **astable** timer (see chart).

Timer type	Function
Monostable	A system that has only one stable state. It can be made to change, but always returns to the same stable state. A push button switch is an example of this. It always springs back out when the pressure is released.
Astable	A system that has no stable state. It changes from one stable state to another all the time. A pendulum is a good example. It swings from one side to the other continuously.

The 555 timer IC is produced as an eight pin unit. Although it is described as a simple IC, it contains 25 transistors, two diodes and 16 resistors! Even though you don't need to know all of the components that make it up, you will need to know inputs and outputs to each of its pins.

1   negative power supply
2   trigger
3   output
4   reset
5   control voltage
6   threshold
7   discharge
8   positive power supply

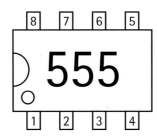

You need to use the chip in the astable mode to create a flashing set of LED lights. This simply involves connecting the pins in a slightly different way from the monostable variation.

When creating this timer circuit it is possible to alter the speed at which the LEDs flash. This is called altering the frequency. The **frequency** is the number of changes each second, and is measured in **hertz** (Hz).

Activity 27: Find as many examples of monostable and astable operations as you can.

As we saw earlier, some circuits are designed using the three main blocks.

This timer circuit has four main blocks.

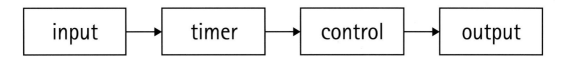

Before you can construct any kind of circuit you need to produce a simple process diagram to show the input, process and output of your electronic system. You will also need to construct a circuit diagram showing the value of the various components that you intend to use.

The block diagram does not accurately represent the actual circuit and the circuit would not physically work in this way. It does, however, help you and others to understand what is going on before you make the circuit.

The diagram below shows the circuit you are going to make using a 555 timer IC and four flashing LEDs. The user of your toy will see only the flashing lights. The circuit itself will be hidden.

Look at the areas that have been labelled as input, timer, control and output. These represent the areas of the simple block diagram for the circuit.

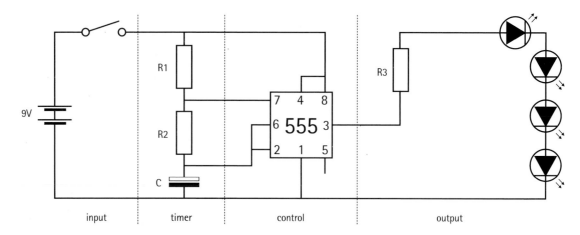

| input | timer | control | output |

As you are using the timer IC to operate your circuit it is possible to alter the timing between the flashes.

Changing the value of the components will affect the frequency of the output.

| Component | Description | Value required to give approximate timings of: | | |
		0.5 second	1.0 second	1.5 seconds
R1	resistor	10 kΩ	10 kΩ	10 kΩ
R2	resistor	120 kΩ	430 kΩ	820 kΩ
R3	resistor	100 kΩ	100 kΩ	100 kΩ
C	capacitor	1.0µF	1.0µF	1.0µF

For the purpose of this circuit you have been given a choice of three different frequencies. You should select the right flash time to suit the type of toy you have decided to make. The third resistor, R3, will remain at 100 kΩ to protect your LEDs from being damaged.

Chemical Etching

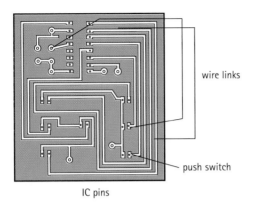

wire links

push switch

IC pins

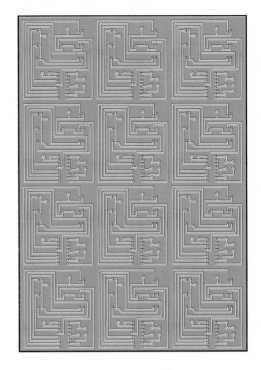

This circuit makes a simple electronic die

Another way to produce a circuit board is to use **chemical etching**. The circuit shown opposite makes a simple electronic die. First the circuit is designed and transferred onto clear plastic sheet by computer, using dry transfers or projector transparency pens used by hand. If a large number are required these can be made in batches.

As with copper track circuit boards the components, chips, resistors and diodes should be put in rows. You should not have wires which cross over.

After peeling off the protective layer, the board is placed in an ultraviolet light box with the clear plastic sheet between the board and the light.

Peeling off the protective layer

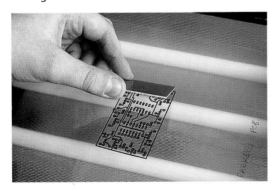

Placing in the ultraviolet light box

Inside the light box the board is being exposed to ultraviolet light

The light box is closed and the light switched on. Different boards require different exposure times. You will need to experiment first or your teacher may tell you how long you need to expose the board for.

The board is now placed in a solution of sodium hydroxide until all the blue has gone. This will take about 2 minutes. Remember to wear rubber gloves and be careful: the chemical can be dangerous.

Placing the board in sodium hydroxide solution

The next stage is to etch the board in a bubble etch tank. The tank contains ferric chloride. Always use gloves and tongs. Place the board in the grid, lower into the tank and switch on.

Safety
- When chemicals are used protective clothing must be worn and an eye bath must be nearby.
- Always wear gloves.

Using a bubble etch tank

Remove the board with tongs and wash thoroughly.

Washing the board

For more on safety see pages 6–7

You can now drill the holes for the components, clean them with wire wool and solder them in place.

The components should be on the top of the board, with the tracks underneath. The circuit for the electronic die can then be put inside a box. The one shown opposite was made by vacuum forming. The designer has used a clever method to fix the lid in place. A thin plastic sheet has been fitted into the base to make a lip.

The finished electronic die with the lid open

Component List

Component	Order code	No for ordering	Cost	Company
LED	UK48C	700	0.05 @ 100+	Maplins
IC Holder	BL19V	100	0.09 @ 50+	Maplins
IC HT2070	AE165	100	0.79 @ 100+	Maplins
Peizo Buzzer	YU87U	100	0.19 @ 100+	Maplins
Batteries AAA	18-0205	60	0.28 @ 20+	Rapid Electronics
Push Switch	78-0100	100	0.095 @ 100+	Rapid Electronics
PCB Board	34-0345	3	15.20 @ 1+	Rapid Electronics
Battery Clip	18-2925	50	0.14 @ 25+	Rapid Electronics

With the lid closed

Test

1 State and explain the safety rules you must follow when using soldering irons.
2 What is a short circuit and how can one be avoided?
3 Name the units used to measure resistance. Draw the symbol for this unit.
4 Why is strip board a good material to build circuits on?
5 Work out how these resistors would be colour coded:

470

360

17k

56k

6 From the colours on the resistors shown below, work out the value for each resistor.

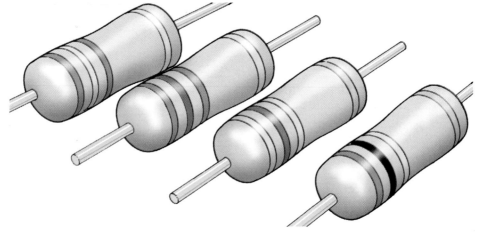

7 What must you do to a soldering iron before you use it?
8 What is special about flux and how does it help you to solder?
9 Describe how you could remove heat from a component when soldering. Why is this important?
10 Why do we use block diagrams when designing and creating circuits?
11 What does IC stand for? Describe what an IC holder is and why it is used in electronics.
12 How can you tell one end of an IC from another?
13 The 555 is a timer chip. It can operate in two ways. Describe these two ways.
14 It is possible to change the speed at which LEDs will flash. What is the speed of flashing called and what units is it measured in?

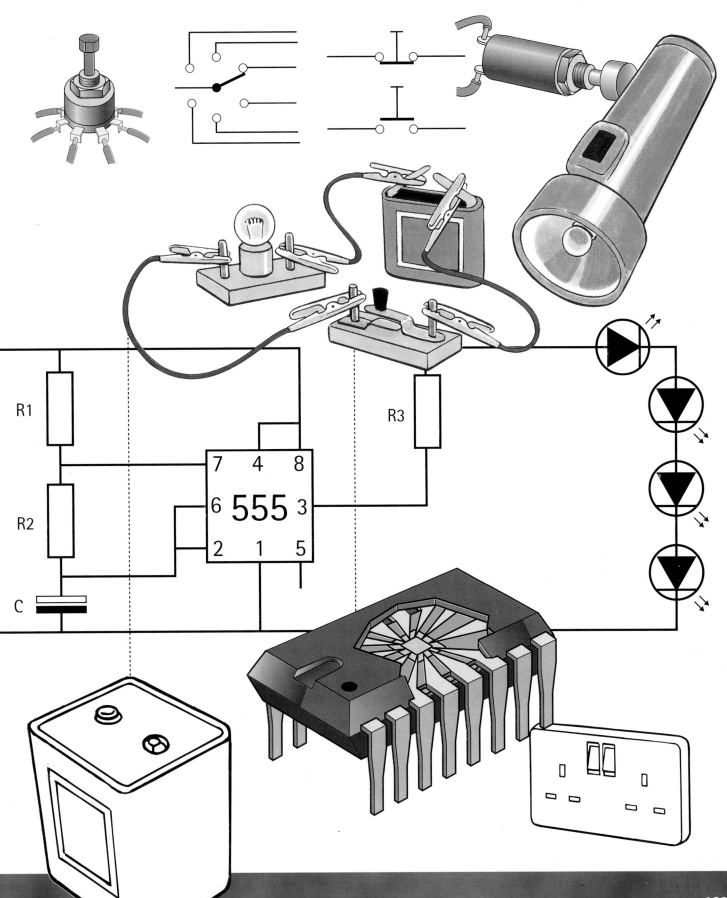

R1

R2

C

7   4   8
6 **555** 3
2   1   5

R3

Metals

Working Metals

All metals have a crystalline structure. If you were to look under a microscope you would see how the surface of the metal has a grain in it.

If you hammer, press or roll metal whilst it is cold, the grain is compressed and distorted. This is called 'work hardening'. If the grains become too distorted the metal will crack and break. You can experiment with this process by bending a piece of wire backwards and forwards.

To stop the material breaking when you work on it, it is best to carry out a process called annealing. To anneal a metal it is heated and then allowed to cool. If you are using copper, cooling can be done by immersing hot metal in cold water. Cooling carbon steel down very quickly has a different effect: the metal becomes brittle and hard. This process is called hardening. We will look at this process in more detail later in the book, but first let us look at the properties of some common metals.

Classifying Metals

Metals can be classified according to a variety of characteristics. They can also be classified according to whether they contain iron or not:
- All **ferrous** metals are iron-based.
- Non-ferrous metals do not contain iron.

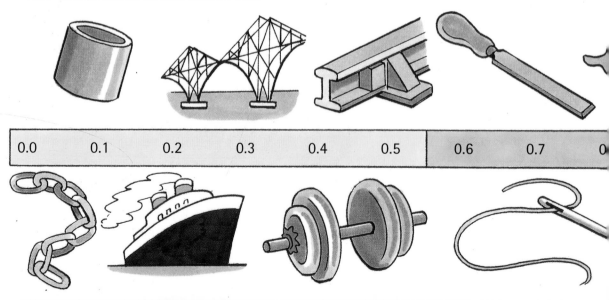

| 0.0 | 0.1 | 0.2 | 0.3 | 0.4 | 0.5 | 0.6 | 0.7 | 0 |

For more on properties of materials see pages 34 and 39–40

Uses of Different Metals

Metal	Ferrous metals			Non-ferrous metals and alloys		
	High carbon steel	Mild steel	Stainless steel	Copper	Brass	Aluminium
Description	Resistant to impact, strong, very hard wearing, hard to shape and work	The most common ferrous material, malleable, strong, easy to work, cheaper than stainless steel or high carbon steel, corrodes easily	Stainless steel contains at least 11% chromium and nickel. Malleable, resistant to corrosion, can be pressed and moulded, gives a clean shiny finish	Ductile, malleable, resistant to corrosion, good conductor of electricity, easily shaped	Brass is an alloy of copper. Malleable, resists corrosion, good conductor of electricity, hard wearing	Malleable, ductile, light, resists corrosion, low density, good conductor of electricity
Uses	Used for tools like drills, files chisels and saws	Used for washing machines, car bodies, nails, screws, nuts and bolts	Used for medical equipment, kitchen equipment	Used for jewellery, wiring, pipes, cooking pots and pans printed circuit boards	Used for door handles, electrical components	Used for aircraft, car wheels, bridges, cans

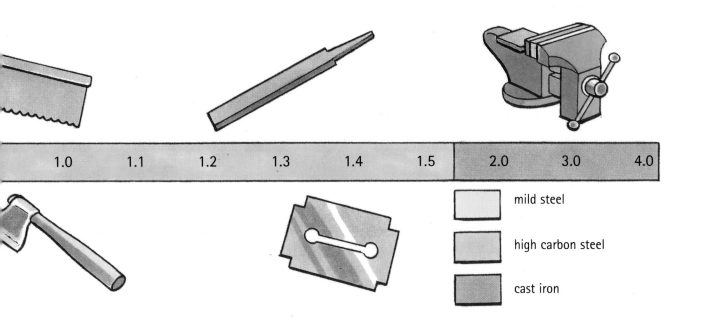

| 1.0 | 1.1 | 1.2 | 1.3 | 1.4 | 1.5 | 2.0 | 3.0 | 4.0 |

mild steel

high carbon steel

cast iron

What type of metal is it made from?

	When dropped on concrete floor	When you file it	When you try to break it	When you grind it
Cast iron	Dull sound	Black powder produced	Snaps easily, large crystalline structure	Dull red sparks
Wrought iron	Slight metallic ring	Hard to achieve smooth finish, file clogs easily	Bends well before breaking. Fibres visible when broken.	Lots of bright sparks
Mild steel	Strong metallic ring	Easy to file	Bends well before breaking with a ragged fracture	Lots of long bright sparks
High carbon steel	A clear high pitch ring	Hard to file – the higher the carbon the harder to file	Snaps with a ringing sound to show a fine silvery structure	Very bright sparks
High-speed steel	A dull metallic ring	Reasonably hard to file	Strong resistance then snaps suddenly	Dull red sparks with a yellowish tinge.

Homework

The knives and forks that you eat your food with are usually made of metal. Decide which metal they are made from and make a list of the properties of the metal that make it suitable for making knives and forks.

The knives and forks that you eat your food with are usually made of metal. What metal could they be made of? Why would your choice of metal be appropriate? What are the properties of the metal that make it suitable? The base of the pillar drill in the school workshop is also made of metal. What metal do you think it is made of? Could the metal you selected for a knife and fork be the same metal used for the base of the pillar drill? If not why not? What are the properties of the metals that make them suitable for the objects in question?

The ballpoint or fountain pen you write with has a metal tip. What metal could it be made of? Why would your choice be appropriate? What are the properties of the metal that make it suitable? The base and table of the pillar drill in the school workshop are also made of metal. What metal do you think they are made of? What are the properties of the metal that make it suitable for the objects in question? Draw a comparison between the two types of metal and the different properties they have, making reference to the required properties of the product in use, and the properties of the metal for manufacture.

Activity 28: Make a list of some metal objects in your home. Next to the name of each object, state what metal you think it is made from and what you think the properties of the metal are that make it suitable for the object.

Making Jewellery

You can make jewellery from a wide range of materials including paper and metals. The best metals for use in a school workshop are copper, brass and aluminium.

Metal	Copper	Brass	Aluminium
Description	Pinkish brown colour, malleable, easy to bend and shape	Gold colour, made with zinc and copper, harder than copper, polishes up well	Silver in colour, polishes up well, malleable, easy to cut and bend, good conductor of heat and electricity
Uses	Used for water pipes and electrical wire	Used for castings, jewellery, tokens, ornaments	Used for drinks cans, cooking foil, jewellery

One of the most important things to think about when designing and making jewellery is **shape**.

Working with Wire

Wire comes in a wide range of types and thicknesses. For jewellery you really need copper or galvanised wire. Wire is usually measured in what are called **gauges**. The larger the gauge number, the thinner the wire.

To make jewellery you will need long nose pliers and wire cutters.

Wire jewellery can be made with all sorts of things from glass to wooden beads to electrical components like resistors and diodes. The wire can be bent to any shape. If you want to produce a specific shape, for example a butterfly brooch, it is best to draw out your design first. Then fix your design onto a piece of wood by hammering a nail into the design at each corner. You have now made what is called a **jig**. It can be used to make as many butterflies as you wish.

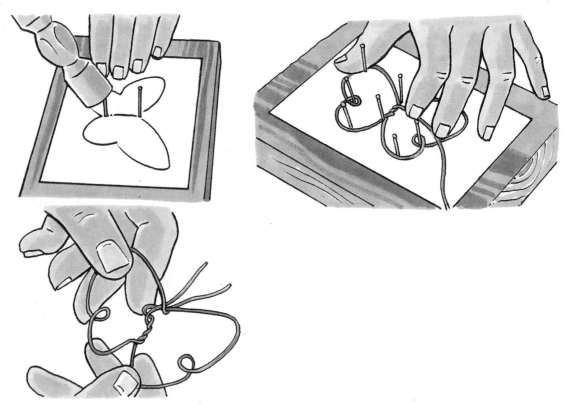

The wire can be soldered using the same techniques as described in the section on soldering electronic circuits, see page 113.

For more on using tools see pages 9–27

Decorating a Wire Shape with Resin

Once made, the butterfly can be dipped in **resin** or placed on a wax sheet and filled with resin.

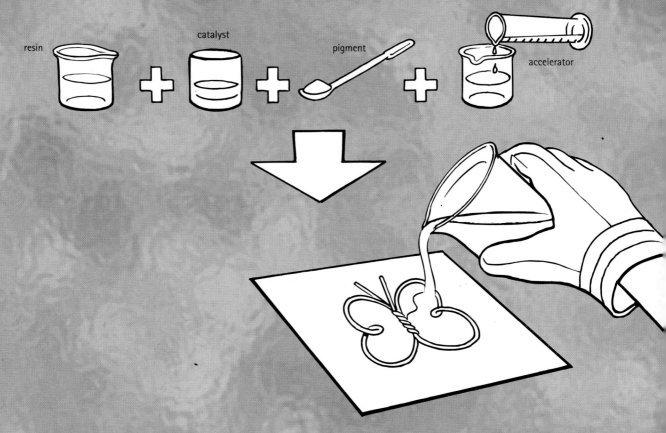

Always wear gloves when working with resins and use the extractor to remove fumes.

Hammered Copper

Before you hammer copper you must anneal it. To do this you heat the copper until it glows cherry red. You then cool it down in water.

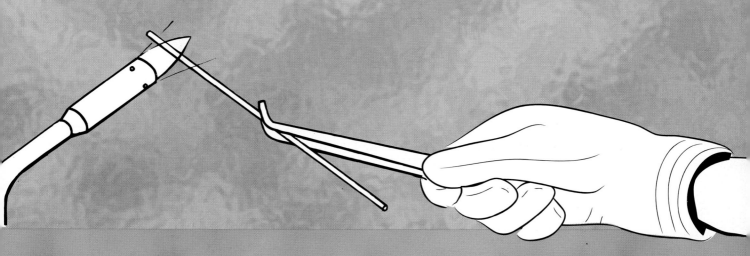

Lengths of soft copper wire and geometric shapes made out of copper sheet can be hammered to form attractive pieces. The hammer blows give the finished copper an interesting finish.

Different hammer heads will create different effects. Hammering on a textured surface can create a different impression. Rusting steel can also produce an interesting surface when hammered. Always work on an **anvil** or metal block.

If you are using copper wire you must keep turning the wire over if you do not want it to curl up.

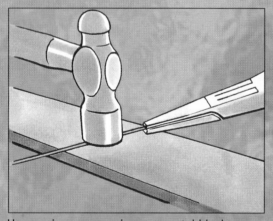

Hammering copper wire on a metal block

Hammering on an anvil

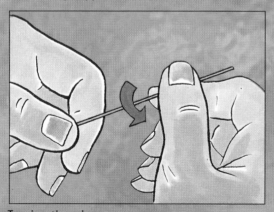

Turning the wire

Bending Wire

By bending wire around pliers, square, triangular and round bars, lots of interesting shapes can be formed. If it is then cut with tin snips or shears, it can be made into interesting chains and links.

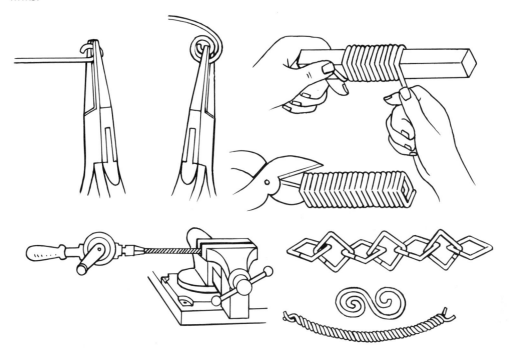

Using Beads and Leather

Wooden and glass beads can be threaded onto copper wire to make attractive pendants and earrings. Leather thongs can be used to create a necklace.

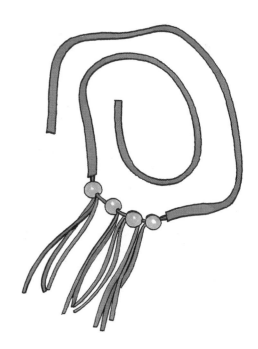

Dream Catchers

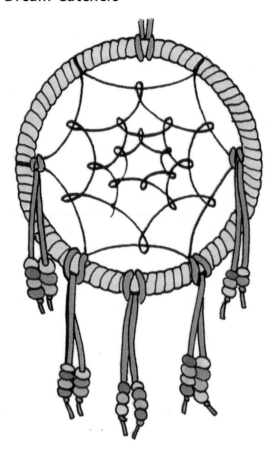

Dream catchers are made with wire, beads and feathers. They are based upon an ancient story told by the Native American Indians. The hoop, with the intricate webbing at its centre, hangs above the bed and ensures a sleep undisturbed by bad dreams.

The central web is said to let good dreams filter through and float down to the sleeper, while bad dreams are entangled in the web and perish at dawn's first light.

Skills Task

Making a Dream Catcher

Dream catchers can be made with wire.

Make a wire hoop and wrap it around with leather, wool or cloth. Glue the ends of the wrapping to fix it in place.

Tie a long piece of cotton to the ring and use half hitch knots to make the web in the centre of the ring. Glue the final knot and cut off any loose cotton.

Add dangles made of leather or twine, putting beads, feathers and other forms of decoration on the hangers. Thread an even number of beads onto each dangle, and then knot the other end.

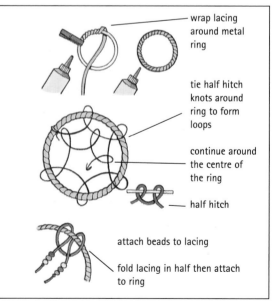

wrap lacing around metal ring

tie half hitch knots around ring to form loops

continue around the centre of the ring

half hitch

attach beads to lacing

fold lacing in half then attach to ring

Enamelling

Enamelling started in 1500 BC when the Egyptians used enamel on bricks and pottery. There are two types of enamel: **synthetic enamel** used in paint and **vitreous enamel**. Vitreous enamel is the fusion of glass on a metal background. This is the type of enamelling used to produce jewellery.

There are four types of jewellery enamel:
- opaque
- transparent
- opalescent
- translucent.

All of these are available in a wide variety of colours and in a powder form called **frit**.

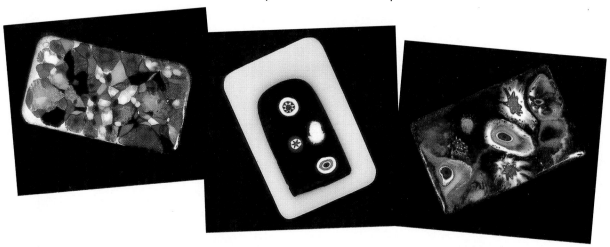

Enamels are made from silica, red lead and potash. The greater the amounts of lead and potash used, the more brilliant the colour, but the softer the enamel.

What Can Be Enamelled?
- **Copper** – this is an ideal metal for enamelling. It is available in sheet, bar, rod, tube, wire and mesh. As it is malleable and ductile it is ideal for jewellery making in the school workshop.
- **Gilding metal** – used in jewellery and some architectural work.
- **Silver** – a special type of silver is used as the melting point of normal silver is close to what is called the fusion-point of enamel.
- **Gold** – this very expensive metal lends itself to enamelling, as can be seen in churches and museums.
- **Steel** – lots of domestic appliances known as 'white goods', including fridges, cookers and washing machines, are enamelled.
- **Aluminium** – this is light, resistant to corrosion and flexible.

Making an Enamelled Brooch

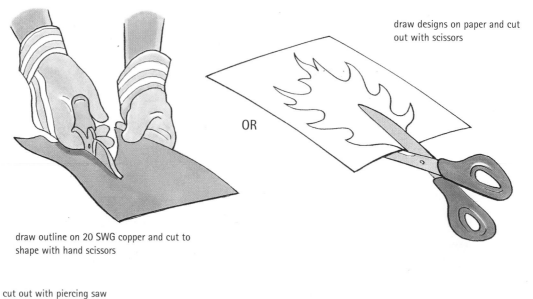

draw designs on paper and cut out with scissors

OR

draw outline on 20 SWG copper and cut to shape with hand scissors

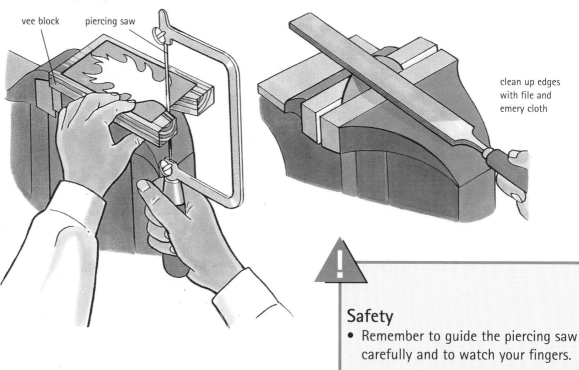

cut out with piercing saw

vee block   piercing saw

clean up edges with file and emery cloth

Safety
- Remember to guide the piercing saw carefully and to watch your fingers.

Draw your design directly onto 20SWG copper and cut it out with hand shears. If the design is complex, draw it onto paper and cut it out with scissors. Then stick it onto the copper and cut out using a piercing saw and vee block (see Section 1).

For instructions on how to use the piercing saw see page 16

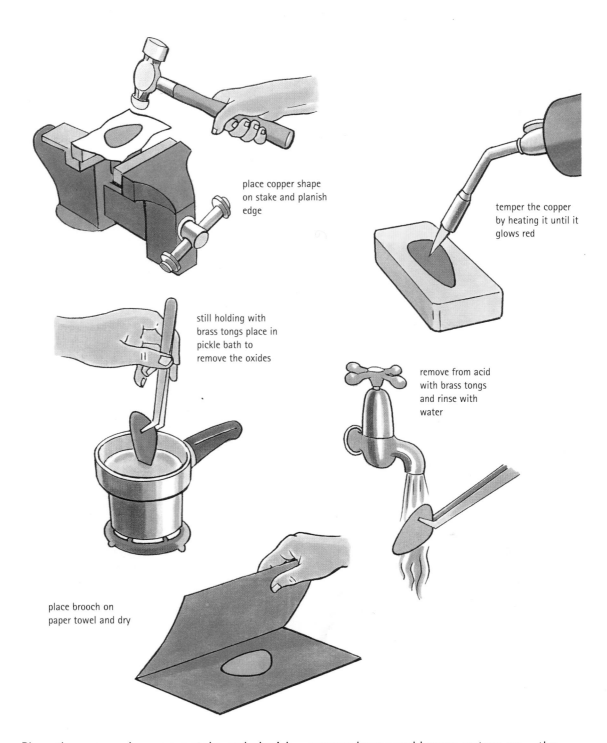

place copper shape on stake and planish edge

temper the copper by heating it until it glows red

still holding with brass tongs place in pickle bath to remove the oxides

remove from acid with brass tongs and rinse with water

place brooch on paper towel and dry

Place the copper shape on a stake and planish – remove lumps and bumps or **true up** – the edges. Then degrease. Temper by heating it until it is dull red, then quench it in water using tongs.

Using the tongs place the shape in a pickle bath to remove the oxides, or clean with wire wool.

Wash well, then dry with a paper towel.

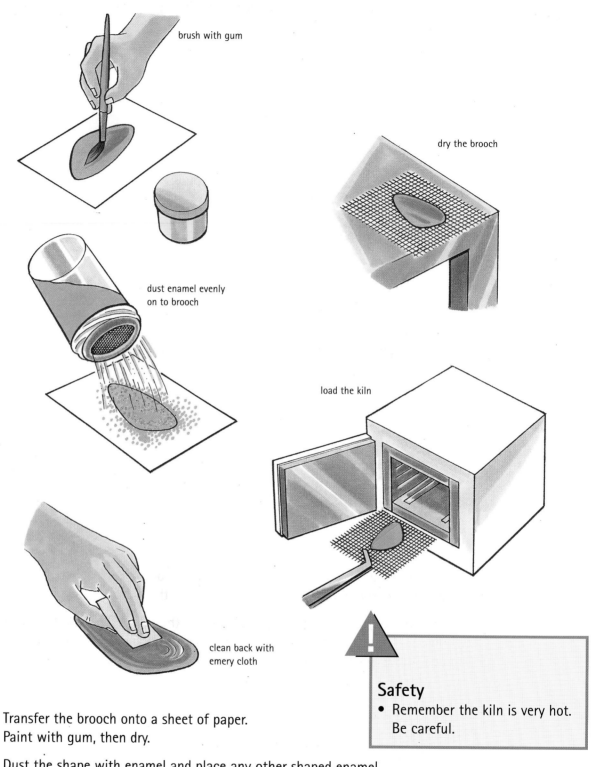

brush with gum

dust enamel evenly
on to brooch

clean back with
emery cloth

dry the brooch

load the kiln

Safety
- Remember the kiln is very hot. Be careful.

Transfer the brooch onto a sheet of paper.
Paint with gum, then dry.

Dust the shape with enamel and place any other shaped enamel
pieces on the brooch. Then place in a preheated kiln for about 1½ minutes.

Finally, finish your product.

Other enamelling effects can be obtained by adding beads and lines of enamel. You can also pull the enamel whilst it is in liquid form.

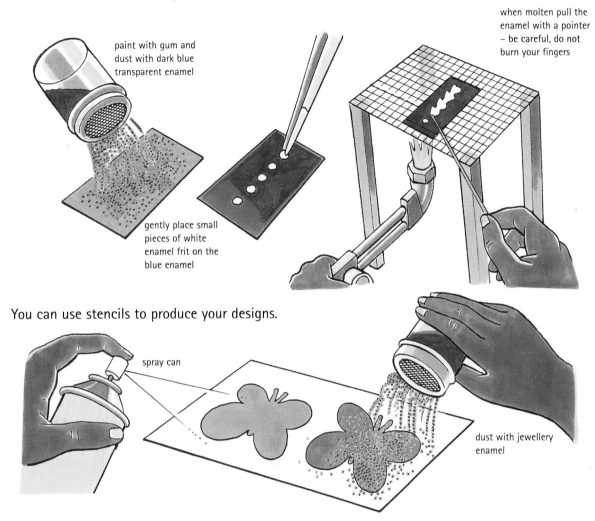

paint with gum and dust with dark blue transparent enamel

when molten pull the enamel with a pointer – be careful, do not burn your fingers

gently place small pieces of white enamel frit on the blue enamel

You can use stencils to produce your designs.

spray can

dust with jewellery enamel

Make a stencil and fix it to the brooch. Spray the brooch with gum and then dust with coloured enamel. Remove the stencil and place the brooch in the kiln.

Once the brooch is enamelled you are ready to fix the pin on the back. This can be done by soldering. The correct name for the pins, necklace clasps and ear wires used on jewellery is **'findings'**. These can be bought in to save you the trouble of making them.

Soldering and Brazing

Soft solder is made from tin and lead. It melts at 185–230 °C.

The type of soft solder used in electronics is cored. That means it has flux built into the wire. This makes it suitable for lightweight work like fixing electrical components. Soft solder is also available in blocks and rods without added flux.

Soft solder uses a hot iron to melt the solder and heat the work. Soldering irons can be electrically heated or heated by a flame.

Silver solder is an alloy of copper, zinc and silver. It melts at 600–800 °C. It is often used in jewellery because it is strong and neat.

Brazing

Some of the softer silver solders can be used with an iron, but usually you would use a brazing hearth to reach the right temperature.

Brazing is sometimes called hard soldering. Brazing rods are made from copper and zinc. They melt at 870–920 °C.

You cannot solder or braze anything without using a **flux**. These are put onto the joint before soldering or brazing. They dissolve any oxides and allow the solder to run freely into the joint. They come ready mixed or as a powder that is mixed with water to make a paste.

Skills Task

Candles of various shapes, colours and sizes are readily available. When designing and making a holder for a candle special care must be taken because of the risk of fire. Broken hollow metal chair and table legs can make ideal candle holders, but they need to be soldered or brazed onto a metal base to prevent the candle from falling over.

Design and make a simple candleholder that incorporates a hollow tube to hold the candle brazed or soldered onto a stable base. When designing your candleholder you need to consider:

- How many candles you wish to hold
- What happens to the molten wax which runs down the candle

Skills Task (continued)

Design and make a simple candleholder that incorporates a hollow tube to hold the candle brazed or soldered onto a stable base. When designing your candleholder you need to consider:

- How many candles you wish to hold
- What happens to the molten wax which runs down the candle
- An appropriate surface finish for your candle holder which will not be damaged when the candle burns away completely.
- How to ensure that your candle holder will not scratch a polished wooden finish on a table.

Design and make a simple candleholder that incorporates a hollow tube to hold the candles. Your candleholder must hold three candles. Your candleholder should reflect a Christmas theme. You should incorporate two different types of metal. You also need to consider:

- Stability to ensure that the holder cannot fall over
- What happens to the molten wax which runs down the candle
- An appropriate surface finish for your candle holder which will not be damaged when the candle burns away completely.
- How to ensure that your candle holder will not scratch a polished wooden finish on a table.

Soldering a Brooch Pin

It is always best to fix the pin above the centre line. This prevents the brooch from tipping over when pinned on your clothes.

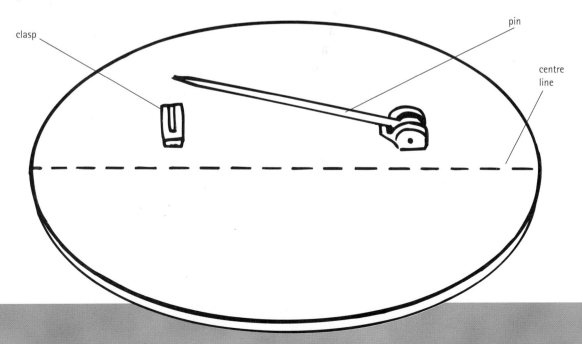

clasp

pin

centre line

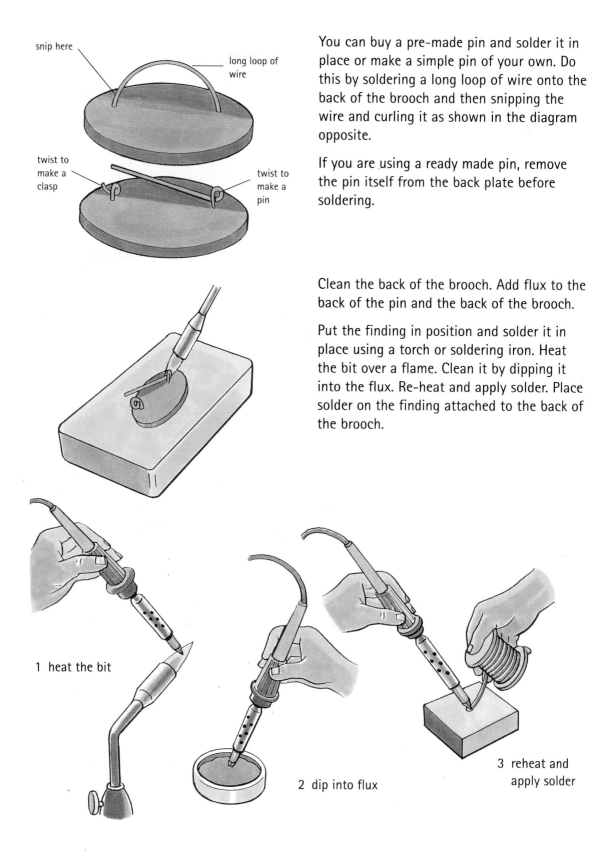

snip here

long loop of wire

twist to make a clasp

twist to make a pin

You can buy a pre-made pin and solder it in place or make a simple pin of your own. Do this by soldering a long loop of wire onto the back of the brooch and then snipping the wire and curling it as shown in the diagram opposite.

If you are using a ready made pin, remove the pin itself from the back plate before soldering.

Clean the back of the brooch. Add flux to the back of the pin and the back of the brooch.

Put the finding in position and solder it in place using a torch or soldering iron. Heat the bit over a flame. Clean it by dipping it into the flux. Re-heat and apply solder. Place solder on the finding attached to the back of the brooch.

1 heat the bit

2 dip into flux

3 reheat and apply solder

For more on using tools see pages 9–27

Activity 29: Draw your own story board to show the enamelling process.

Test

1 What does the phrase 'work hardening' mean and why is it important?
2 Explain the difference between ferrous and non-ferrous metals.
3 List the properties of aluminium. What is it used for?
4 Describe the main differences between copper, brass and aluminium.
5 What does annealing mean? How would you anneal a piece of copper?
6 What is enamelling?
7 Using sketches and notes explain the process of enamelling.
8 What is a stencil and when can stencils be useful?
9 Explain the differences between soft soldering, silver soldering and brazing.
10 Describe why you need to use flux when soldering.

Design Brief

Using your knowledge of metal and enamelling design a badge to recognise sporting achievement.

Using your knowledge of metal and enamelling design a prize which can take the form of a trophy or badge to recognise sporting achievement. Your sporting prize must reflect a single sport.

Design a trophy that could be used to recognise outstanding sporting achievement for the disabled Olympics. The trophy must incorporate enamel and reflect both the chosen sport and the world-wide nature of the disabled Olympics. You should consider quality, use of colour, shape and form.

Section 7

Product Evaluation

Product Development

Products are continually changing and evolving through:
• the development of new materials
• new ways of making things
• technological advances
• fashion changes.

Critical Analysis

In this section of the book, you will build upon your knowledge of the materials and processes used in the manufacture of a number of everyday products. You will also learn how to carry out a **critical analysis** of a product. This is when you explore how a product is made, what it is made of and how well the product works.

Of course there are a number of ways of looking at how well a product works. To the manufacturer and shopkeeper who sold the product, what is important is how many units are sold and how much profit they made. The customer judges the product by how well it does the job or maybe on the basis of other factors like how environmentally friendly the product is. Fashion also plays an important part here; we often buy things because we want to keep up with our friends or the latest trends.

Ergonomics
The scientific study of how people use things is called **ergonomics**. Ergonomics looks at our senses like touch, sight, smell and hearing and the way we use products physically. This enables designers to make products that we like to feel, touch, look at and hold. Fashion trends are often driven by our senses. The way we enjoy a product or choose it in the first place is also affected by these same senses. You will need to understand these things before you can design products effectively. The best way to learn about them is to look at and study products that you use every day.

Anthropometrics
Of course products are of no use unless they are the right size for the user. A worktop that is too high or low, a handle that is too big to fit your hand and a pair of spectacles that do not fit round your head are all badly designed products. The study of the average sizes of people is called **anthropometrics**. Without this type of study designers would not be able to make chairs, telephones and everyday items that fit us.

For more on ergonomics and anthropometrics see pages 32–33

Evaluating from Different Points of View

In order to evaluate a product properly you need to think of each person in the chain from the designer to the end user.

Person in the chain	Designer	Manufacturer	Shopkeeper	End user
Requirements	The designer could be the manufacturer or an outside consultant. The product has to be designed to be made and sold.	The manufacturer needs to build upon the equipment and skills of its workforce.	The shopkeeper needs to receive the goods in perfect working order and maintain them until they are sold.	Products designed for young people differ from those designed and made for elderly people.
Questions to ask	• Does it fit current fashion trends? • Will the manufacturer like it? • Does it use standard parts? • What are the manufacturing costs?	• Can I make it at the right price? • Do I need to buy new equipment? • Who else makes products that do the same job? • How will it be transported to the shop? • Will it help my reputation in the market place?	• Is it fashionable? • How much profit is there? • How easy is it to get more if they sell? • Who else is is selling them and for how much money? • Does the manufacturer have a good backup for repairs?	• Can we afford it? • Will it do the job? • How easy is it to maintain? • Is is strong? • Is it safe? • How well has it been made? • Is it good value for money? • Does the manufacturer have a good reputation? • Does it meet British Standards?

Activity 30: Make a table like the one shown above. Using an everyday product of your choice, write down a list of questions that could be used to judge how well the product has been designed. Remember: questions need to be devised for each of the four people involved in the design and use of your chosen product. You may find it helpful to identify the age and background of the end user first.

Product History

Another important way to understand a product, and why it was designed in a particular way, is to study its history. Understanding the past is a vital part of understanding the present. If you meet a new friend, telling them the things you like to do (which are always based on your experiences of the past) is a very important part of explaining who you are and what you are like. A large amount of the past is still with us today, in the objects and buildings that have survived.

Case Study – the History of the Domestic Iron

Early Irons

The domestic iron has been around for hundreds of years. It has evolved like all products by changes in its use, new technology and fashion trends. The Romans used wooden presses to press their clothes, but it was the Chinese who introduced the first real iron and the idea of smoothing clothes in the eighth century. They used a smoother, which looked like a small saucepan. The Vikings brought the idea of ironing to Britain in the ninth century, using stones shaped like mushrooms.

Sad Irons

The irons we use today probably started in the sixteenth century. Early flat irons called 'sad' irons were made of cast iron. The word sad means to make firm or stiff. The local blacksmith manufactured irons, usually casting each as a one off.

Cast iron is strong, has a high tensile strength, is tough and can be moulded easily when molten. It has a high density, is a good conductor of heat and was readily available to blacksmiths.

Sad irons were heated by placing them on the oven or by an open fire. They were big bulky things for two reasons. Firstly, they needed to retain heat. Secondly, they needed to be heavy to iron out the creases in coarse cotton and linen. To see if they were hot enough, the end user, who was usually a maid, would spit on the base of the iron.

Imagine how hot the cast iron handle of a sad iron would get. The maid would have to wrap a piece of cloth around the handle of the iron to stop it burning her hand. People who could not afford a maid would usually take their clothes to the local washing house or cleaners. As lace became popular, smaller cast iron lace irons were produced. There are still a large number of flat irons about. They were built to last!

As the irons became more popular in the seventeenth century they were produced in batches – usually by sand casting. One of the main disadvantages of sad irons was that they would transfer soot and dirt from the fire

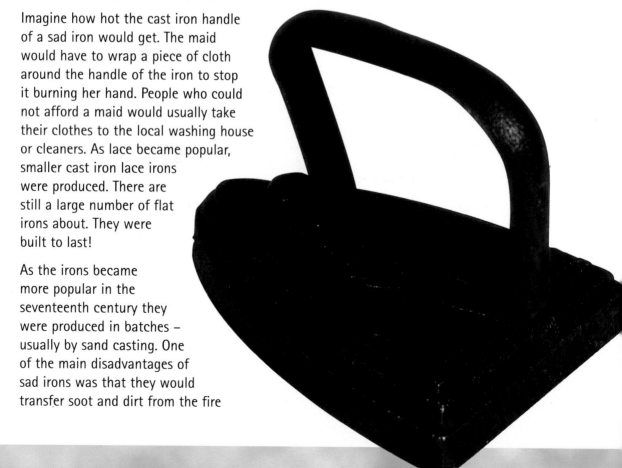

onto the clean clothes. To overcome this problem, designers users soon invented base plates that clipped onto the base of the iron before it was used. The base plates were usually made of aluminium or steel as these materials have good heat conductivity and were malleable so they could easily be bent, pounded or rolled into a shape that would fit the sad iron. Aluminium was also good as it does not rust, although it has a much lower resistance to scratching than the cast iron body of the sad iron.

Box Irons

Another disadvantage with the flat iron was the need to keep warming the iron up. Most houses would have a number of flat irons so that one could be warming whilst another was being used. Special stoves were designed to heat up the irons.

The box iron was the next type of iron to be invented. Box irons were not put on the fire, but were heated from inside by a hot 'slug'. These materials retained the heat better than the cast iron and were cheap to produce. The slug was made of charcoal, steel or stone.

A designer changed the shape and style of the flat iron by adding a wooden handle. The most famous iron, and very fashionable at the time, was the Mrs Potts Cold Handle Sad Iron, made in 1871. Wood is a poor conductor of heat, unlike the cast iron used to make the main body of the iron. The wooden handle protected the hands of the user from burns. Wood is also more comfortable to hold. The cost of manufacture increased, as the amount of labour needed to make the iron had increased. There were now a number of parts to make separately and assemble.

To cut costs manufacturers started to use standard parts – handles that could be used on more than one iron base. The good news for the end user was that having one handle assembly and lots of bases reduced costs overall as only one iron was needed.

Unfortunately, the sad iron still had one major drawback. It cooled down as soon as it was removed from the fire or stove. It was not long before new ideas were put to the test and a new type of box iron was invented, the charcoal or ember iron.

Charcoal and Ember Irons

Charcoal and ember irons worked by lighting a fire inside the iron itself. Petrol, charcoal, alcohol, methylated spirits, naphtha, vegetable oil and paraffin irons were all invented and then a real breakthough arrived with the advent of gas.

Gas Irons

Gas irons became very popular in Britain as the number of families doing their own ironing increased. Maids were becoming expensive, so the end user of the common iron changed.

Most families now had an iron of their own. The family, not the maid, did the ironing, although steam laundries continued to exist in most towns. With the change of end user came a change in the needs of the designer and manufacturer. More irons were needed and fashion trends became even more important.

Electric Irons

Electric irons, first invented in 1880, were slow to catch on at first. They were expensive to buy, awkward and heavy to use. The fashion was to use gas irons, even though they were dirty and very dangerous.

As people started to travel more the electric iron started to become more popular, especially amongst the new middle class. Soon, the new electric revolution was making its mark across the country.

Electric irons were lighter than the original flat irons, helped partly by developments in Bakelite and steel fabrication. The base plate became the only component cast in cast iron, and even this was soon replaced with a fabricated steel base.

New developments in electric technology enabled the elements in the new electric irons to be hotter and better controlled, so the user did not need to press as hard and was less likely to burn the clothes. The need to replace the electric element when it burned out changed the design of the iron. Ease of maintenance – how easy it was to take the iron apart to repair it – was now an additional consideration.

Steam Irons

Then another breakthrough happened, the incorporation of steam. Steam enables creases to be removed from fabric more easily. Irons became lighter still. Advances made in plastic technologies and manufacturing processes led to a revolution in the style of the domestic iron. They are now available in a wide range of colours, styles and anthropometrically designed shapes.

What about the future – will we need irons or will new technologies in fabrics lead to iron free clothing?

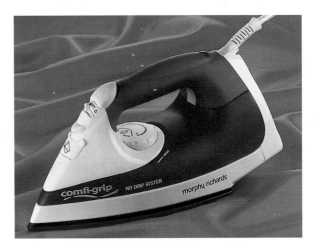

Product Factors

When you come to buy something you often have a choice of a range of different solutions. When you are making a choice you should consider the following:

Price

There are a number of factors affecting the price of an object. There is not only the price of the object itself to consider, but running costs and maintenance costs.

- Some products are designed to last for a very long time, others are made to be thrown away after a short period of time.
- Some products need very little maintenance or cleaning, others require regular maintenance.
- Some products can be maintained by the user, others need to be returned to the manufacturer to be maintained.

Technical Factors

Ensuring the product meets correct technical factors is an essential part of choosing the right product:

- how easy the object is to use?
- how reliable is it?
- how safe is it?
- what colour is it available in?
- how convenient it is to use?
- ergonomics – does it fit?

Service Factors

Another reason for selecting one product over another is the quality of service provided by the seller. This includes things like:

- delivery
- guarantees
- availability of the product
- instructions
- reliability of the supplier
- quality of sales and service.

Fashion

Fashion and advertising plays a very important part in product choice.

- Do you like the shape of the object?
- Is it the right colour?
- It is a well-known make?

For more on communicating your designs see pages 28–32

Other Factors

There are wide range of values related to culture, social and moral attitudes that affect the choice of products.

- it is it made from recyclable materials?
- in which country was it made?
- who made it and did they get paid a fair price for their work?

Homework

Think of an object that you have bought in last couple of months. Was there a choice between alternatives? What made you choose this particular item? Use as many specialist terms as you can.

Draw a chart to show a range of considerations that need to be taken into account when you are choosing a product. These considerations should include emotional response, appearance, function, ease of use and price. Your chart can be illustrated using cut-outs or pictures from magazines and product brochures.

There are number of ways to buy products. One is to buy on sheer instinct. An other is to think through carefully what your needs are before you ever go to the shop. Draw a chart to show a range of thoughts/points that need to be taken into consideration when you are choosing a product. The chart must compare three compatible products. List the advantages and disadvantages of each product. For each design consideration state whether the information can be obtained before visiting the shop through brochures, advertising and catalogues, can be obtained before purchase in the shop, or would be determined by use.

Product Comparison

Another way to evaluate a product is to compare it with other products made to do the same job. You can try out each one in turn and then pick the one you like best.

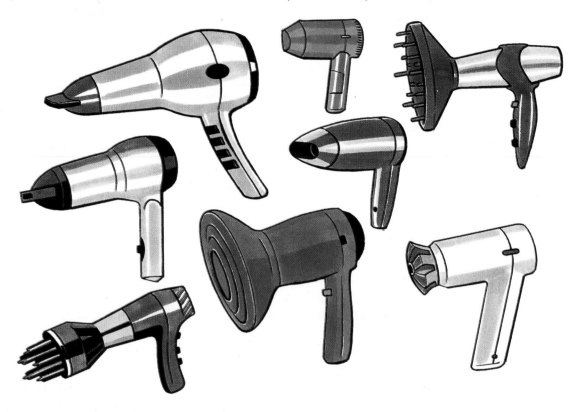

Carrying Out a Product Investigation

The first stage in carrying out a product investigation is to pick an object that interests you. You can use the Internet, libraries and museums to study the history of your chosen product. Advertisements in old newspapers and trade magazines contain large amounts of product detail.

Next, you need to research the answers to a series of questions:
- What is the main use of the product?
- Where will it be used?
- Where will it be stored?
- What sort of people would want to purchase it?
- What effect does it have on people's lives?
- Who designed it first?
- Why was it designed?
- What is it made from?
- Have the materials it is made from changed over the years?
- How is it made?

Products are designed to be used by someone. In the case of the irons, the user changed from maids in wealthy households to family members in every household. In researching and testing a product you must look at:

- **Ergonomic factors** – these include colour, shape and any other factors such as sound, taste and smell which affect the way the end user interacts with the product.
- **Anthropometric factors** – these include shape and size which affect the suitability for the end user.
- **Fashion** – how the success or failure of the product depends on fashion trends and competition from other similar products.

Analysing Materials

In the design and manufacture of products, a number of factors affect the choice of materials used. These include:

- the **properties** of the materials, for example strength or resistance to damage
- **cost**
- the **availability** of the materials
- the **manufacturing processes**: suitability for shaping or forming, suitability for assembly including permanent and temporary joining, the number of processes required in the manufacturing process
- **end user** (or customer) **preference**
- **environmental** considerations, including source, recyclability, biodegradability, fashion and trends.

Product Life Expectancy

Consumers are often influenced by the life expectancy of a product, and the degree of maintenance that is required. One of the reasons manufacturers select certain materials over others is the maintenance requirements of particular materials. Another factor is how the product can be **recycled** or **disposed** of at the end of its life.

When investigating how products are made you can consider how the life of a material can be extended through:

- selection of appropriate materials, thinking about maintenance, cleaning and lubricating
- the use of finishes
- ability to replace vulnerable parts or components.

You can also investigate how products can be disposed of when their useful life is over. Think about:

- recycling, such as melting down the raw materials and reforming them
- reusing, such as disassembling the product and using the parts
- disposal, such as incineration.

Product Manufacture

It is important that you learn to recognise how materials can be worked to manufacture a desired shape or form. Other sections of this book will help you to do this. You need to understand how manufacturing practices, such as casting, moulding and fabricating, affect the final design of a product. You will also need to learn how this information can be used to help you to design your own products.

In designing and manufacturing a product it is important to consider strength to weight ratios and how materials can be manufactured to use minimal materials whilst gaining maximum strength.

Processes you need to know about are:
- shaping by **wastage** – cutting, filing, planing, grinding
- shaping by deforming – vacuum forming, injection moulding, die-casting, press forming, blow moulding.

In selecting materials and manufacturing processes cost is important:
- cost of raw materials
- cost of manufacture including labour, techniques and number of stages to process
- cost of minimising the hazards involved in manufacturing.

You also need to understand how manufacturing processes are continually developing:
- as new products are developed
- as new manufacturing methods are developed
- as new materials are developed
- as manufacturers compete with each other.

As large scale manufacturing becomes more and more common, the amount of scrap, waste and pollution becomes even more important. You can judge a product on the basis of the amount of scrap, waste and pollution that is produced during its manufacture.

Scrap
It is scrap from materials like aluminium, plastics, steel and wood that manufacturers cannot use. For example, the wood that is left over when you have cut the shape you want from a sheet will not be useful. Computers can help reduce scrap by positioning pieces on the sheet so that the amount left over is as small as possible. This also saves money.

In injection moulding the scrap is the runners and sprues that result from the moulding process and products that do not meet the quality standards set by the manufacturer. These can sometimes be ground down and reused.

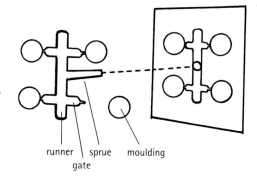

runner sprue moulding
gate

When you look at a product think about how it was made. How many pieces does it have? Are these pieces cut out of a single piece of material or moulded?

Waste

Waste is the products we throw away after they have gone out of fashion, worn out or broken. Some of this waste can be recycled, but most tends to be buried in **landfill sites**. Part of the problem is the need to separate waste like steel, aluminium, plastic and glass so that it can be recycled. Most products contain a wide range of materials and are not easy to take apart.

When you evaluate a product think about how much of the product could be recycled and reused. How responsible is the consumer for breaking down waste products so that they can be recycled? Should manufacturers be thinking about recyclability when they design a product?

Pollution

Pollution occurs because of both the need to manufacture products and the need to dispose of scrap and waste. Air, sound, water and land pollution are all problems for modern society. Manufacturing processes have been found to pollute through:

- Fumes from paint, glue and cleaning solvents
- Burning oil-based fuels called hydrocarbons, producing fumes
- When chemical processes are used to turn oil into plastics, chemical waste is produced
- Leaking tanks
- Disposal of waste oils and chemicals
- The chemicals produced from decomposing waste in landfill sites
- Burning fossil fuels, producing carbon monoxide
- Burning fossil fuels at high temperatures produces nitrogen oxides
- When rubbish or fuel is burnt sulphur oxides are produced
- Lead and heavy materials are serious pollutants.
- Low level ozone can result when pollutants react together. When sunlight supplies the energy that causes pollutants to react together, the pollution is said to be **photochemical**. Carbon particles from smoke are called **particulates**.

When you examine a product think about the pollution that the manufacture of the product has produced. Could this have been improved at the design stage.

The Manufacturer

The size of an organisation has been shown to affect the degree of its environmental impact. A manufacturing company producing 20 000 bicycles per day will probably affect the environment more than one producing 100 bicycles a day. This is not because larger manufacturers do not care about the environment, but because the production and waste will be concentrated. The environment will find it harder to correct any imbalances caused.

A number of manufacturers now practise what is called **environmentally soft manufacturing**. They think about the number of products needed and scale their production carefully. They try to use renewable energy and follow a code of ethics.

When you evaluate a product think about the scale of production, how the product was made, where the product was made and how environmentally friendly the product is.

Materials

Another way of testing a product is to look at the materials used and to devise and carry out a number of tests to establish the suitability of the materials used.

If you are able to get a small sample of the material used you could try:
- bending the material back and forth until it fails (testing **fatigue strength**)
- testing the ability of the material to withstand scratching, water or heat
- bending the material to different degrees to see if it returns to its original strength (testing **elasticity**)
- stretching the material until it breaks.

Looking Around

As you use products you should always be looking at how they are made, what they are made of and how well they work. Our experiences with everyday objects can teach us how things work and how to be a good designer and discerning consumer.

Activity 31: Look at the range of everyday objects shown below. How could they be improved? What materials are they made from? What manufacturing processes have been used to make them?

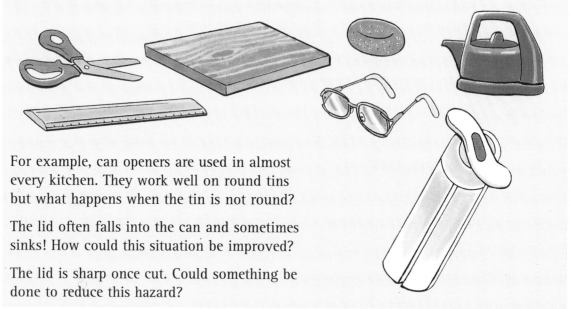

For example, can openers are used in almost every kitchen. They work well on round tins but what happens when the tin is not round?

The lid often falls into the can and sometimes sinks! How could this situation be improved?

The lid is sharp once cut. Could something be done to reduce this hazard?

Activity 32: Choose one of the types of object listed and undertake your own product case study:

- telephones
- radios and stereos
- road transport
- shoes and trainers.

Test

1 Describe the main reasons why products develop and change.
2 What are ergonomics and anthropometrics?
3 Describe why it is important for designers to look at a product's history before designing new products.
4 List five key questions that should be asked when studying a product.
5 How can you analyse the materials a product is made from in order to determine their properties?
6 What does the term 'product life' mean and why is it important?
7 Describe the difference between the terms 'scrap' and 'waste'.
8 What are the main causes of pollution?
9 Why are the manufacturing processes and scale of production important for the environment?
10 Why is recycling more difficult if a product cannot easily be disassembled?

Glossary

Alternating Current	Electricity pulsing in both directions, e.g. your home electricity supply.
Anneal	To heat treat a metal to make it soft and easy to work.
Anthropometrics	Data about the different measurements of people used to help design products.
Astable	Having no stable state.
Bakelite	The trade name of an early type of plastic named after its inventor L Baekeland.
Bearing	A component used to reduce friction and wear where there are moving parts in a machine.
Brace	A component that can be added to a structure to give it strength by triangulation.
Brazing	A type of soldering using copper and zinc to join metals.
Calendering	A manufacturing process where a warm dough of material is passed between rollers to produce a thin film or sheet of material.
Cam	A mechanical device used to change rotary motion into reciprocating or oscillating motion or to change the direction of reciprocating motion.
Capacitor	An electronic component used to store electricity.
Casting	A manufacturing process where material in a fluid state is poured into a mould.
Chemical Etching	A manufacturing method of producing electronic circuit boards.
Chipboard	A type of manufactured board made by gluing wood chips together.
Chopping	Removing large chips of material using a chisel and mallet.
Chuck	A device used in machines to hold drill bits and other cutting tools.
Composite	A type of material made by combining more than one material to give better properties.
Compression Strength	The ability of a material to resist crushing.
Conductivity	The ability of a material to conduct (allow through) heat or electricity.
Crank	A lever attached to a rotating shaft or wheel.
Deforming	A method of manufacture where material is twisted, bent, stretched or compressed into a new shape.
Density	A measure of how closely packed something is – how solid it is.
Die	A tool used to form materials. The die will match the shape wanted.
Diode	An electrical component called a semiconductor because it controls or restricts the flow of electricity through it.
Direct Current	Electricity flowing continuously in one direction.

Draught	A taper put on a mould or former to help the operator to remove the newly formed component
Drill bit	A cutting tool used to drill holes.
Ductility	A property of a material showing how easy it is to change its shape by bending, twisting, stretching and shearing.
Effort	The input needed on a lever or machine to make it move.
Elasticity	A property of a material that shows how well it can be stretched, twisted and bent and still return to its original shape.
Elastomer	Any rubber type substance.
Electronics	The use and design of products incorporating electrical components.
Electroplating	The use of electricity to coat metal with a thin protective plate.
Enamel	The fusion of glass onto a metal surface.
Environmentally soft manufacturing	A type of manufacturing which promotes a natural environment free from pollution.
Ergonomics	Designing objects for people to use.
Extruding	A manufacturing process where material is fed through a hopper, heated and forced through a shaping mould to form a long section of material. Similar to meat put through a mincer.
Fabrication	A manufacturing process where a product is built from different pieces of material.
Ferrous	Metals that contain iron as the primary element.
Findings	The name given to pins and clasps used in jewellery making.
Flux	A material used to help solder or metals flow.
Former	A tool used repeatedly to form a piece of material into a desired shape.
Forming	The process of reshaping materials.
Frequency	How often something happens.
Frit	Mixed material used for making glass and in enamelling.
Fulcrum	The pivot point on a lever.
Galvanising	To coat iron or metals with zinc.
Gear	A wheel with teeth or pegs used to transmit motion or force.
Grain	The patterns in wood created by the way the tree has grown.
Gusset	A component used in structures to add strength to corners.
Hardwood	A type of wood that comes from deciduous trees like oak, teak and walnut.
Information Communication Technology (ICT)	The use of computers and information technology.
Injection Moulding	A manufacturing process where material is heated and forced through a nozzle into a mould.

Integrated Circuit	A single electronic component incorporating a number of other components.
Lacquer	A finish like paint used to protect materials.
Laminating	Adding a thin veneer to enhance surface properties.
Lever	A type of machine incorporating an input, fulcrum and output.
Light Emitting Diode	A semiconductor diode used in electronic circuits.
Load	The output of a lever.
Malleability	The ability of a material to be rolled, pounded or bent into shape.
Manufactured Board	A material made by a manufacturing process as opposed to a naturally formed material.
Mechanical Advantage	The use of mechanisms to achieve improved output, e.g. a lever to increase the amount of force applied.
Microelectronics	The miniaturisation or use of miniaturised electronic components and circuits.
Monostable	Having one stable state.
Moulding	A manufacturing process used to form material into a new shape.
Oscillating movement	Moving back and forth in a curved path, e.g. a swing.
Paring	The use of a chisel to remove small shavings from wood.
Particulates	A type of air pollution consisting of tiny particles of carbon floating in the air.
Photochemical Pollution	Pollution caused by sunlight acting on chemicals in the atmosphere, e.g. low level ozone.
Polymer	Identical small molecules linked to form a larger molecule.
Polymerisation	The process of joining small molecules to make a larger molecule.
Process Diagram	A diagram used to show the various stages of manufacture.
Pulley	A grooved wheel used to lift heavy weights.
Ratchet	A device that only allows movement in one direction.
Reciprocating Movement	Moving in one direction and then the other in a straight line.
Resin	A substance made from sap or polymerisation, which is used in the production of plastics.
Resistance	How well a material resists the flow of electricity, heat or fluids.
Resistor	An electronic component that resists electricity.
Rotary Movement	Circular movement about a fixed point.
Scrap	An output from manufacturing that cannot be reused easily or economically.
Shear	A force attempting to cut the object it is acting upon.
Shell Structure	A type of structure where the material is shaped to enhance its strength, e.g. a car body.
Softwood	Type of wood that comes from coniferous trees that bear cones, for example pine and fir trees.

Solder	A substance used to join metals and electronic components.
Standard Stock	Common shapes, sizes or weights produced for convenient use by manufacturers.
Taper	An angle on a mould to help the operator to remove the manufactured component.
Temper	To heat treat metals to make them more malleable.
Tension	The force acting upon a structure when it is pulled or stretched.
Thermoplastic Material	A material that softens when heated and can be formed into shape. When reheated it can be reformed into a new shape.
Thermosetting Material	A material that cannot be reshaped once it has been formed.
Torsion	A twisting force.
Veneer	A thin slice or layer of material used to enhance the surface of a product.
Vitreous	Consisting of or like glass.
Washer	A component used with nuts and bolts to spread a load and prevent the nuts and bolts from unscrewing themselves.
Waste	Material that is thrown away rather than being used.
Wedge	A device that converts a forward motion into a splitting motion acting at right angles to itself.
Work Hardening	A description used to describe what happens when a material gets harder the more it is worked.

Tools

Anvil	Glass paper	Rip saw
Belt sander	Glue gun	Screwdriver, slotted, Philips, Posidrive
Bench hook	Hacksaw	Scribe
Buffing machine	Hand drill	Sliding bevel
Chisel	Long nose pliers	Soldering iron
Circular saw	Marking gauge	Spanner
Coping saw	Nail punch	Steel rule
Cross cut saw	Odd leg callipers	Tenon saw or back saw
Disc sander	Piercing saw	Try square
Dividers	Plane	Vibrating plate sander
Dovetail saw	Power drill	Workbench
Engineer's square	Power plane	
File	Rasp	

Index